Become a top fact-fetcher with CGP!

Quick question — do you own CGP's Knowledge Organiser
for Foundation Level AQA GCSE Combined Science?

You do? Great! Now you can use this Knowledge Retriever
to check you've really remembered all the crucial facts.

There are two memory tests for each topic, plus mixed quiz questions
to make extra sure it's all stuck in your brain. Enjoy.

CGP — still the best! ☺

Our sole aim here at CGP is to produce the highest quality books —
carefully written, immaculately presented and dangerously close to being funny.

Then we work our socks off to get them out to you
— at the cheapest possible prices.

Contents

Required Practicals

Practical Skills

Published by CGP.
From original material by Richard Parsons.

Editors: Ellen Burton, Laura Collins, Emily Forsberg, Emily Garrett, Luke Molloy and George Wright
Contributor: Paddy Gannon

With thanks to Luke Bennett, Katie Fernandez and Glenn Rogers for the proofreading.
With thanks to Emily Smith for the copyright research.

ISBN: 978 1 78908 496 2

Printed by Elanders Ltd, Newcastle upon Tyne.
Clipart from Corel®
Illustrations by: Sandy Gardner Artist, email sandy@sandygardner.co.uk

Text, design, layout and original illustrations © Coordination Group Publications Ltd (CGP) 2020
All rights reserved.

Photocopying this book is not permitted, even if you have a CLA licence.
Extra copies are available from CGP with next day delivery. • 0800 1712 712 • www.cgpbooks.co.uk

How to Use This Book

Every page in this book has a matching page in the **Knowledge Organiser** for GCSE Combined Science. Before using this book, try to **memorise** everything on a Knowledge Organiser page. Then follow these **seven steps** to see how much knowledge you're able to retrieve...

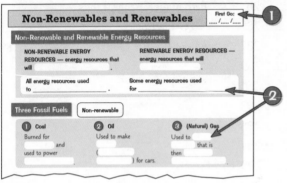

1 In this book, there are two versions of each page. Find the **'First Go'** of the page you've tried to memorise, and write the **date** at the top.

2 Use what you've learned from the Knowledge Organiser to **fill in** any dotted lines or white spaces.

You may need to draw, complete or add labels to diagrams too.

3 Use the Knowledge Organiser to **check your work**.
Use a **different colour pen** to write in anything you missed or that wasn't quite right. This lets you see clearly what you **know** and what you **don't know**.

4 After doing the First Go page, **wait a few days**. This is important because **spacing out** your retrieval practice helps you to remember things better.

5 Now do the **Second Go** page.
The Second Go page is harder — it has more things missing.

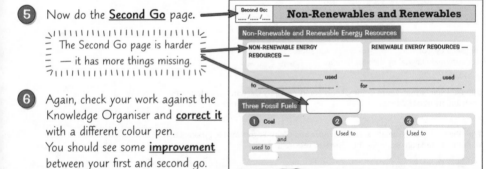

6 Again, check your work against the Knowledge Organiser and **correct it** with a different colour pen.
You should see some **improvement** between your first and second go.

7 **Wait** another few days, then try recreating the whole Knowledge Organiser page on a **blank piece of paper**. If you can do this, you'll know you've **really learned it**.

There are also **Mixed Practice Quizzes** dotted throughout the book:
• The quizzes come in sets of four. They test a mix of content from the previous few pages.
• Do each quiz on a different day — write the date you do each one at the top of the quiz.
• Tick the questions you get right and record your score in the box at the end.

The Scientific Method

Developing Theories

Come up with *hypothesis*

↓

test hypothesis

↓

Evidence is peer-reviewed

↓

If all evidence backs up
_____ , it
becomes an
official theory .

HYPOTHESIS — a possible ~~outcome~~
for _____ .

PEER REVIEW — when other scientists check results
and explanations before _____ .

_____ can still change
over time _____ ,
e.g. the theory of atomic structure:

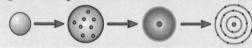

Models

REPRESENTATIONAL MODELS — a simplified _____
of the _____ , e.g. the molecular model of matter:

Models help scientists explain
_____ and
make _____ .

COMPUTATIONAL MODELS — computers are used to _____ complex processes.

Issues in Science

_____
can create four issues:

1. Economic — e.g. beneficial
_____ , like alternative energy
sources, may be too _____ to use.

2. Environmental — e.g. _____
could _____ the natural environment.

3. Social — _____ based on research can
affect people, e.g. _____ fossil fuels.

4. Personal — some decisions affect
_____ , e.g. a person
may not want a wind farm being built
_____ .

Media reports on scientific developments may be
_____ , inaccurate or _____ .

Hazard and Risk

HAZARD — something that could
_____ .

RISK — the _____ that a
_____ will cause harm.

Hazards associated with
science experiments include:

e.g. sulfuric acid

Faulty _____
equipment

_____ from Bunsen burners

The seriousness of the _____ and
the likelihood of _____
both need consideration.

4

The Scientific Method

Developing Theories

Come up with [   ]

⬇

[   ]

⬇

Evidence is [   ]

⬇

If
[   ]

HYPOTHESIS — [   ]

PEER REVIEW — [   ]

[   ] can still change
over time [   ],
e.g. [   ] :

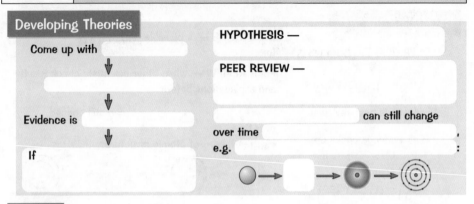

Models

REPRESENTATIONAL MODELS — a [   ]
[   ], e.g. [   ] of matter:

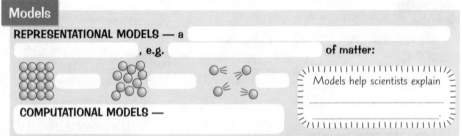

Models help scientists explain
....
....

COMPUTATIONAL MODELS — [   ]

Issues in Science

[   ]
can create four issues:

① Economic — [   ]

② [   ]

③ Social — [   ]

④ Personal — [   ]

.... on scientific
developments may be ....

Hazard and Risk

HAZARD — [   ]

RISK — [   ]

.... associated with
science experiments include:

[   ]

[   ]

[   ]

The ....
....
both need consideration.

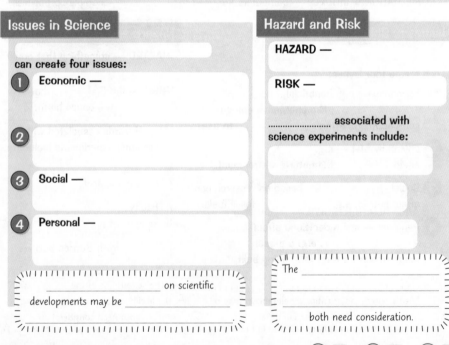

Working Scientifically

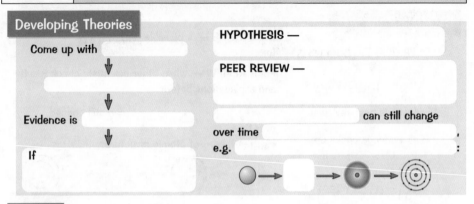

Designing & Performing Experiments

Collecting Data

Data should be...

REPEATABLE	Same person gets .... after repeating experiment using the .... and equipment.
....	Similar results can be achieved by ...., or by using a different method or piece of ....
ACCURATE	Results are ....
....	All data is close to ....

Reliable data is .... and ....

Valid results are .... and .... and answer the ....

Fair Tests

INDEPENDENT VARIABLE	Variable that you ....
.... **VARIABLE**	Variable that ....
.... **VARIABLE**	Variable that is ....
....	An experiment kept under .... as .... without anything being done to it.
....	An experiment where only .... changes, whilst all other variables are kept ....

.... are carried out when .... can't be controlled.

Four Things to Look Out For

1. **RANDOM ERRORS —** .... caused by things like .... in measuring.
2. **SYSTEMATIC ERRORS —** measurements that are wrong by ....
3. **ZERO ERRORS —** systematic errors that are caused by using .... that isn't ....
4. **ANOMALOUS RESULTS —** results that .... with the rest of the data.

Anomalous results can be .... if you know ....

Processing Data

Calculate the .... — add together .... data values and .... number of values.

UNCERTAINTY — the amount by which a .... may differ from the ....

$$\text{uncertainty} = \frac{\text{..........................}}{\text{..........................}}$$

.... value minus ....

In any calculation, you should round the answer to the .... number of significant figures (s.f.) given.

Working Scientifically

Second Go: ...../...../..... Designing & Performing Experiments

Collecting Data

	Data should be...	Reliable data
	Same person gets	
	Similar results can	Valid results

Fair Tests

_____ can't be controlled.

INDEPENDENT VARIABLE —

— an experiment kept under the
— an experiment where

Four Things to Look Out For

1 RANDOM ERRORS —

2 SYSTEMATIC ERRORS —

3 ZERO ERRORS —

4 ANOMALOUS RESULTS —

Anomalous results _____
_____ .

Processing Data

_____ —
add together _____
_____ and divide by
_____ .

UNCERTAINTY —

uncertainty = _____

In any calculation, _____
_____ .

Presenting Data

Bar Charts

Bar charts are used when independent variable is [_____] or [_____].

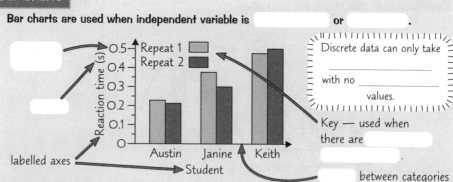

Repeat 1
Repeat 2

[_____]

[_____]

labelled axes

Reaction time (s)

0.5
0.4
0.3
0.2
0.1
0

Austin   Janine   Keith

Student

Discrete data can only take

with no _____

values.

Key — used when there are [_____]

[_____].

[_____] between categories

Plotting Graphs

Graphs are used when [_____] variables are [_____].

_____ data — can take _____ within a range.

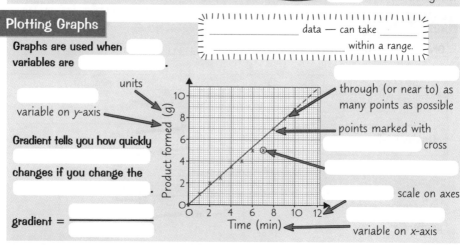

units

[_____]

variable on y-axis

Gradient tells you how quickly

[_____]

changes if you change the

[_____].

gradient = [_____]

Product formed (g)

10
8
6
4
2
O

O 2 4 6 8 10 12

Time (min)

through (or near to) as many points as possible

points marked with [_____] cross

[_____] scale on axes

[_____]

variable on x-axis

Three Types of Correlation Between Variables

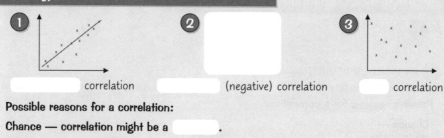

1

[_____] correlation

2

[_____] (negative) correlation

3

[_____] correlation

Possible reasons for a correlation:

Chance — correlation might be a [_____].

Third variable — another [_____] links the [_____].

Cause — if every other variable that could affect the result is [_____], you can conclude that changing one variable causes the [_____].

 ☑   ☑   ☑

Working Scientifically

Presenting Data

Bar Charts

Bar charts are used when [ ]
[ ] .

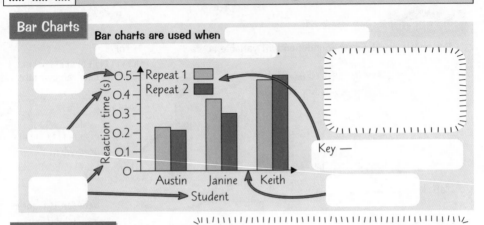

Key — [ ]

Plotting Graphs

Graphs are used when [ ]
[ ] .

[ ] — can take [ ]
[ ] .

Gradient tells you

gradient = [ ]

(or near to) [ ]

variable on [ ]

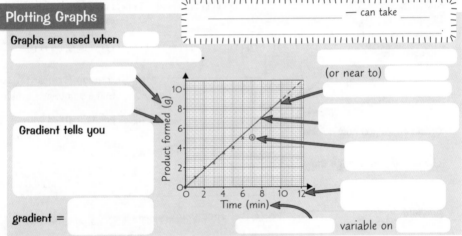

Three Types of Correlation Between Variables

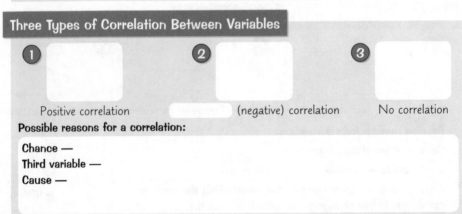

1   Positive correlation

2   [ ] (negative) correlation

3   No correlation

Possible reasons for a correlation:

Chance —
Third variable —
Cause —

Conclusions, Evaluations and Units

Conclusions

Draw conclusion by stating [_____] between [_____] variables.

⬇

Justify conclusion using [_____].

⬇

Refer to [_____] and state whether [_____].

You can only draw a conclusion from [_____] — you can't go any further than that.

Evaluations

EVALUATION — a [_____] of the whole investigation.

	Things to consider
[_____]	• Validity of [_____] • [_____] variables
Results	• [_____], accuracy, [_____] and [_____] of results • Number of [_____] taken • Level of [_____] in the results
[_____] results	• Causes of any [_____] results

You could make more predictions based on [_____], which you could test [_____].

Repeating experiment with changes to improve the [_____] will give you more [_____] in your conclusions.

S.I. Units

S.I. BASE UNITS — a set of [_____] that [_____] use.

Quantity	S.I. Unit
	kilogram ( )
length	( )
	second ( )
temperature	(K)

Scaling Units

SCALING PREFIX — a word or [_____] that goes [_____] a unit to indicate a [_____].

Multiple of unit	Prefix
10^{12}	[_____] (T)
10^9	( )
	[_____] (M)
	kilo ( )
0.1	[_____] (d)
	centi ( )
0.001	[_____] ( )
	micro ( )
10^{-9}	[_____] (n)

kg ⇄ g

÷1000 ⬆⬇ ×1000

dm^3

÷1000 ⬆⬇ ×1000

Second Go:
..... / ..... / .....

Conclusions, Evaluations and Units

Conclusions

Draw conclusion by _____

_____ .

⬇

_____

⬇

Refer to _____ .

You can only draw a conclusion from _____ — you can't _____ .

Evaluations

EVALUATION — _____

_____ .

	Things to consider

Repeating experiment _____

You could _____ based on your conclusion, _____

S.I. Units

S.I. BASE UNITS —

Quantity	S.I. Unit
	kilogram (kg)
length	

Scaling Units

SCALING PREFIX —

Multiple of unit	Prefix
	deci (d)
	centi (c)

g

dm³

Mixed Practice Quizzes

You've reached the conclusion of this topic. Time to evaluate your knowledge of p.3-10 by working through the following quiz questions methodically. I'll stop now.

Quiz 1 | Date: ...... / ...... / ......

1) Give the equation used to find the gradient of a line on a graph. ☑
2) When can anomalous results be ignored? ☑
3) Give two ways in which models can be useful to scientists. ☑
4) Which term is given to a possible explanation for an observation? ☑
5) What is an evaluation? ☑
6) Give two examples of S.I. base units,
   and the quantities they are used to measure. ☑
7) What two things must be considered when assessing a hazard? ☑
8) Give three features of a bar chart. ☑
9) How can you calculate the uncertainty of a mean value? ☑
10) When might you need to carry out a control experiment? ☑

Total:

Quiz 2 | Date: ...... / ...... / ......

1) What is the range of a set of data? ☑
2) How is the mean of a set of results calculated? ☑
3) True or false? Bar charts are often used to display experimental results where the independent variable is discrete. ☑
4) Why can accepted theories still change over time? ☑
5) State the S.I. base unit for temperature. ☑
6) True or false? A conclusion cannot go beyond what the data shows. ☑
7) What is a dependent variable? ☑
8) Which type of model shows a real system as a simplified picture? ☑
9) Name three types of experimental errors. ☑
10) Give two types of issue that can result from scientific developments. ☑

Total:

Mixed Practice Quizzes

Quiz 3   Date: ...... / ...... / ......

1) Give three hazards associated with science experiments.
2) What makes an experiment a fair test?
3) What is meant by the term 'S.I. base unit'?
4) Give one issue related to media reports about scientific developments.
5) How is repeatable data different to reproducible data?
6) What is peer review?
7) Give two reasons why a correlation may arise between two variables, even if changing one variable doesn't cause the other to change.
8) True or false? The independent variable is shown on a graph's y-axis.
9) Give an example of an impact of a scientific development on individuals.
10) What is meant by the 'uncertainty' of a result?

Total:

Quiz 4   Date: ...... / ...... / ......

1) True or false? A risk is something that could potentially cause harm.
2) Give two things you should consider about your method when you're writing an evaluation.
3) Would it be better to use a bar chart or a graph to present the results of an experiment in which both variables are continuous?
4) What are random errors in an experiment?
5) Which scaling prefix indicates a multiplying factor of 0.001?
6) Give an example of an accepted theory that has changed over time.
7) Define the term 'systematic error'.
8) What is a control variable?
9) Define each of the following terms:
   a) Accurate data
   b) Precise data
   c) Valid results
10) Describe how to draw a line of best fit on a graph.

Total:

Cells

Eukaryotic Cells

Animal **CELL**

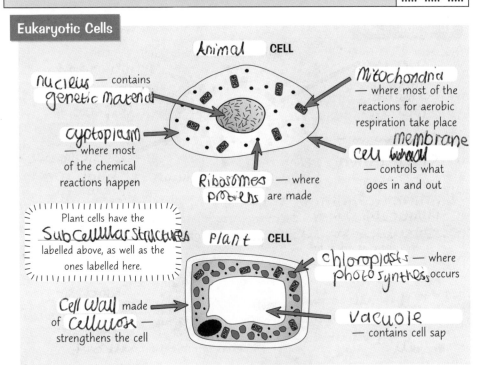

nucleus — contains
genetic material

cytoplasm
— where most
of the chemical
reactions happen

Ribosomes — where
proteins are made

Mitochondria
— where most of the
reactions for aerobic
respiration take place

membrane
Cell wall
— controls what
goes in and out

Plant cells have the
Sub cellular structures
labelled above, as well as the
ones labelled here.

Plant **CELL**

Cell Wall made
of Cellulose —
strengthens the cell

chloroplasts — where
photosynthesis occurs

vacuole
— contains cell sap

Prokaryotic Cells

Bacteria **CELL**

(tiny compared to eukaryotic cells)

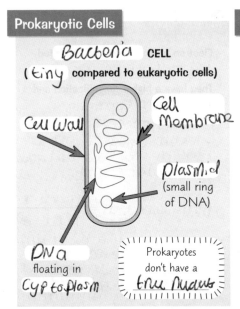

Cell Wall

Cell
Membrane

plasmid
(small ring
of DNA)

DNa
floating in
Cytoplasm

Prokaryotes
don't have a
true nucleus

Microscopy

Erecton microscopes were
invented later than light microscopes.
They have a higher Magnification
and resolution than light
microscopes — they let us see
smaller things in more detail,
meaning we can understand
subcellular structures better now.

$$\text{Magnification} = \frac{\text{image size}}{\text{real size}}$$

Use Standard form to
write really small numbers.
E.g. 0.0045 = 4.5×10^{-3}

Cells

Eukaryotic Cells

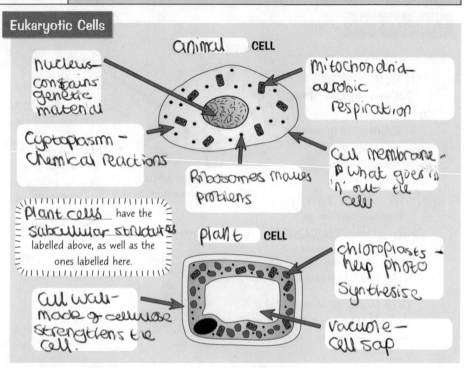

animal CELL

nucleus— contains genetic material

Mitochondria— aerobic respiration

Cytoplasm — Chemical reactions

Cell membrane— what goes in 'n' out the cell

Ribosomes makes proteins

Plant cells have the subcellular structures labelled above, as well as the ones labelled here.

plant CELL

chloroplasts — help photosynthesise

Cell wall— made of cellulose strengthens the cell.

Vacuole— cell sap

Prokaryotic Cells

bacteria CELL

(tiny compared to eukaryotic cells)

Cell wall

Cell membrane

Plasmid rings of dna

Dna floating in cytoplasm

prokaryotic cells don't have a true nucleus

Microscopy

Electron microscopes were invented before light microscopes. They have a higher magnification and Resolution than light Microscopes. This makes smaller things easier to look at so we understand subcellular structures better

$$magnification = \frac{image \; size}{real \; size}$$

Use standard form to write really small numbers
E.g. $0.0045 = 45 \times 10^{-3}$

Cell Division

Chromosomes and the Cell Cycle

CHROMOSOMES — coiled up lengths of **Dna Molecules** which carry **genes**.
They're found in the **nucleus**, and they're normally in **pairs in body cells**.

CELL CYCLE — a series of stages in which **cells divide** to produce **new cells**.

Before **a cell divides**, it does three things:

1 **grows in size**.

2 Increases the amount of **subcellular structures**
e.g. **mitochondria** and **ribosomes**.

3 **duplicate** its DNA.

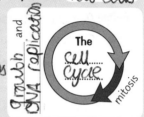

The **Cell**
Cycle

growth and DNA replication

mitosis

Mitosis

MITOSIS — the stage of the cell cycle when the **cell divides**.

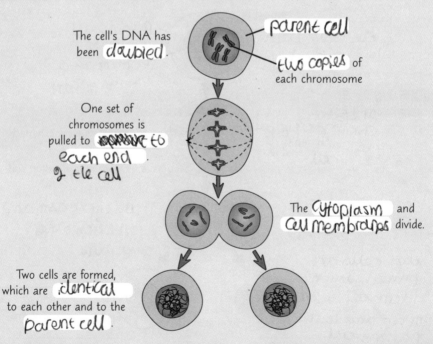

The cell's DNA has been **doubled**.

parent cell

two copies of each chromosome

One set of chromosomes is pulled to ~~appear to~~ **each end of the cell**

The **cytoplasm** and **cell membrane** divide.

Two cells are formed, which are **identical** to each other and to the **parent cell**.

Mitosis allows **multicellular organisms** to grow
or replace cells that **are damaged.**

Topic B1 — Cell Biology

Cell Division

Chromosomes and the Cell Cycle

CHROMOSOMES — Coiled up lengths of DNA molecules, carry genes.
They're found in the nucleus, normally in pairs in body cells.

CELL CYCLE — .

Before a cell divides, it does three things:

1. grows in size
2. Increases the amount of subcellular structures
3. Duplicates its DNA.

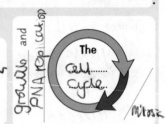

growth and DNA replication

The Cell..... Cycle.

Mitosis

Mitosis

MITOSIS — Stage of the cell cycle when the cell divides.

the cells DNA is doubled

Parent cell

two copies of the chromosome

One set of chromosomes is pulled to each end of the cell

the cytoplasm and all membranes divide

two cells are formed which are identical to each other and to the parent cell

Mitosis allows multicellular organisms to grow or replace or cells that have been damaged.

Topic B1 — Cell Biology

Cell Specialisation

Cell Differentiation

DIFFERENTIATION — the process by which a Cell changes to become specialised for its job.
In most animal cells , the ability to differentiate is lost at an early stage , but many plant cells never lose this ability.

Five Types of Specialised Cells

1. Sperm cell — reproduction

long tail and streamlined head for swimming to the egg.

2. Nerve cell — rapid signalling

Long to cover a large distance and branched to form a network of connections

3. Xylem and phloem — transporting substances

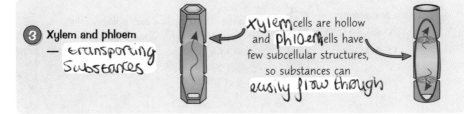

xylem cells are hollow and phloem cells have few subcellular structures, so substances can easily flow through

4. Muscle cell — contraction

Long so they have space to contract and lots of mitochondria for energy.

5. Root hair cell — absorbing water and minerals

Large surface area for absorbing water and mineral ions from the soil.

Topic B1 — Cell Biology

Cell Specialisation

Cell Differentiation

DIFFERENTIATION — the process by which a cell changes to become specialised for its job.

In most animal cells , the ability to differenciate is lost at an early stage, but many plant cells never lose this ability.

Five Types of Specialised Cells

1 Sperm cell —
Reproduction

Long tail and streamlined head for swimming to the egg.

2 Nerve cell —
rapid signalling

Long to cover a large distance and branched to form a network of connection

3 Xylem and phloem —
transporting substances

Xylem cells are hollow and phloem cells have few sub cellular structures so substances can easily flow through

4 Muscle cell —
contraction

Long so they have space to contract, and lots of mitochondria for energy.

5 Root hair cell —
absorbs water + minerals

Large surface area for absorbing water and mineral ions from the soil.

Mixed Practice Quizzes

Time for some quiz questions to test how much you can remember from p.13-18.

Quiz 1 — Date: ...... / ...... / ......

1) How are muscle cells specialised for their function? long room to contract . ✓
2) What does a cell's nucleus contain? DNA / genetic material ✓
3) True or false? Animal cells have a cell wall. false ✓
4) Which cells are bigger: eukaryotic cells or prokaryotic cells? eukaryotic ✓
5) What is a chromosome? ✳ ☐
6) Give three things that a cell does before it divides by mitosis. ✳ ☐
7) How have electron microscopes allowed scientists to better understand subcellular structures? more magnification + resolution ✓
8) True or false? Most animal cells lose the ability to differentiate at an early stage. ✳ ☐
9) In microscopy calculations, when should standard form be used? big with big numbers ✓
10) Why do sperm cells have a long tail and a streamlined head? swim to the egg ✓

Total: 7/10

Quiz 2 — Date: ...... / ...... / ......

1) What is the function of xylem and phloem cells? transport substances ✓
2) Which cells have DNA enclosed in a nucleus: eukaryotic cells or prokaryotic cells? eukaryotic ✓
3) Where in a cell do most chemical reactions take place? ✳ ☐
4) What is the cell cycle? ✳ ☐
5) What is the function of a cell membrane? what goes ← → the cell ✓
6) How are nerve cells specialised for their function? long for connections ✓
7) What is cell differentiation? ✳ ☐
8) How are sperm cells specialised for their function? long tail, streamline head ✓
9) True or false? Mitosis produces four identical cells. ✗ ☐
10) What do you divide the size of an image by to find its magnification? the size of the real size ✓

Total: 6/10

Topic B1 — Cell Biology

Mixed Practice Quizzes

Quiz 3   Date: ...... / ...... / ......

1) Name a type of cell that is specialised for contraction. Muscle cell ✓

2) What process allows multicellular organisms to grow
and to replace cells that have been damaged? Mitosis ✓

3) Were electron microscopes invented before or after light microscopes? ✓
before

4) In which subcellular structure are proteins made? ✳ Ribosome

5) What name is given to a small ring of DNA in prokaryotic cells? ✳ plasmid

6) What does the permanent vacuole of a plant cell contain? ✳ Cell sap

7) During mitosis, where do the two sets of chromosomes
move to before the cell divides?

8) What is the name for the process by which a cell changes
to become specialised for its job?

9) Name a type of cell that is specialised for absorbing water and minerals.

10) What are plant cell walls made from?

Total:

Quiz 4   Date: ...... / ...... / ......

1) During which stage of the cell cycle do cells divide?

2) Name one structure found in plant cells that is not found in animal cells.

3) True or false? Electron microscopes have a lower magnification
and resolution than light microscopes.

4) Where does photosynthesis occur in plant cells?

5) Where is DNA found in a bacterial cell?

6) Where in a cell do most of the chemical reactions
for aerobic respiration take place?

7) Why is mitosis important in multicellular organisms?

8) True or false? Chromosomes are normally in pairs in body cells.

9) How are root hair cells specialised for their function?

10) How many identical cells are formed
from a single parent cell during mitosis?

Total:

Topic B1 — Cell Biology

Stem Cells

Stem Cells

STEM CELLS — [ ], which can divide to produce lots more [ ], and can [ ] into many other types of cell.

Three sources of stem cells:

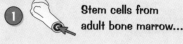

1 Stem cells from adult bone marrow... ...can become... ...[ ], e.g. blood cells.

2 [ ] ...can become... ...any kind of human cell.

3 Stem cells from plant meristems... ...can become... [ ].

Uses of Stem Cells

Stem cells can be grown in a [ ] and made to differentiate into [ ] cells:

Uses in plants:

Produce [ ] of whole plants [ ],

e.g. to grow more plants of a rare species, or clone crops with [ ].

Uses in medicine:

E.g. stem cells could produce [ ] to treat [ ], or insulin-producing cells to treat [ ].

In [ ], an embryo could be made with the [ ] as the patient — then stem cells used from the embryo wouldn't be rejected by the patient.

Risk: stem cells from the lab could ...., which could get transferred to the ....

Topic B1 — Cell Biology

Stem Cells

Stem Cells

STEM CELLS —

Three sources of stem cells:

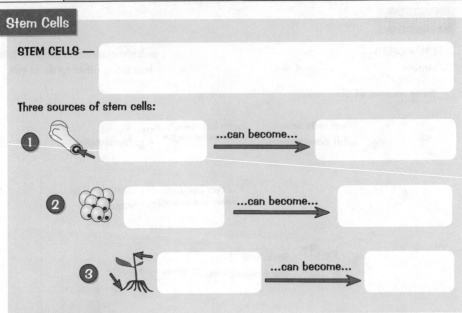

1 [blank] ...can become... [blank]

2 [blank] ...can become... [blank]

3 [blank] ...can become... [blank]

Uses of Stem Cells

Stem cells can be [blank] and [blank] cells:

Uses in plants:

Uses in medicine:

Risk: stem cells from the lab could ....,
which ....

Transport in Cells

Diffusion

DIFFUSION — the spreading out of [   ]
from an area of [   ]
to an area of [   ].

Only very [   ] (e.g. oxygen,
glucose) can diffuse through [   ].

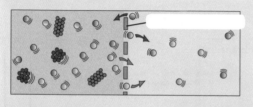

These three factors [   ] the rate
of diffusion across a [   ]:

1 A high [   ]
(e.g. loads of the [   ] on
one side and hardly any on the other).

2 [   ]

3 A [   ] surface area.

Osmosis

OSMOSIS — the movement
of [   ] molecules across
a [   ]
[   ] from a region of
[   ]
to a region of [   ]
[   ].

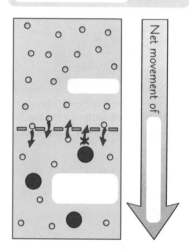

Net movement of [   ]

Active Transport

ACTIVE TRANSPORT — the [   ] of a substance against the
[   ]. Unlike diffusion and osmosis,
it requires [   ]. It allows...

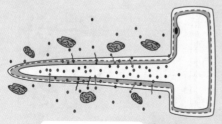

... [   ] (for plant
growth) to be absorbed from the
soil into [   ].

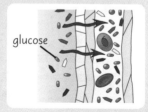

glucose

... [   ] (for cell respiration)
to be absorbed into the
[   ] from the [   ].

Transport in Cells

Diffusion

DIFFUSION —

Only

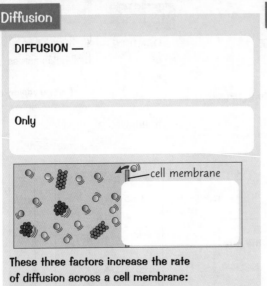

cell membrane

These three factors increase the rate
of diffusion across a cell membrane:

1 (e.g. loads of the

).

2

3

Osmosis

OSMOSIS —

Active Transport

ACTIVE TRANSPORT —

It allows...

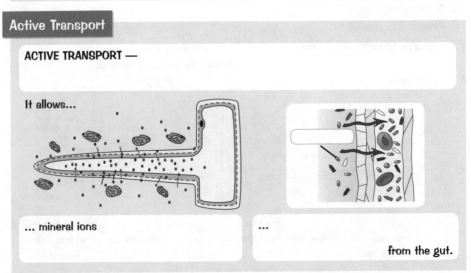

... mineral ions

...

from the gut.

Exchanging Substances

Surface Area to Volume Ratio

Single-celled organism

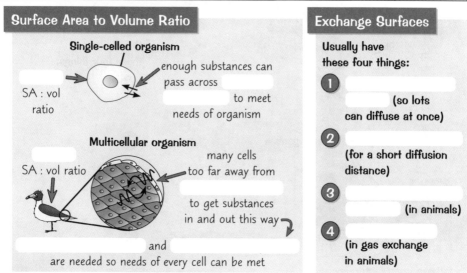

[____] SA : vol ratio

enough substances can pass across [____] to meet [____] needs of organism

Multicellular organism

[____] SA : vol ratio

many cells too far away from [____] to get substances in and out this way

[____] and [____] are needed so needs of every cell can be met

Exchange Surfaces

Usually have these four things:

1 [____] [____] (so lots can diffuse at once)

2 [____] (for a short diffusion distance)

3 [____] (in animals)

4 [____] (in gas exchange in animals)

Four Organs Adapted for Exchange

1 [____] — gas exchange

[____] shape

[____] let gases in and out

2 [____] — gas exchange in fish
([____] move between water and blood)

Lots of [____], covered in [____]

[____] have lots of [____]

[____] have a surface layer of cells

3 [____] — absorption of food molecules from gut to blood

Single layer of [____]

Covered in [____]

[____] network

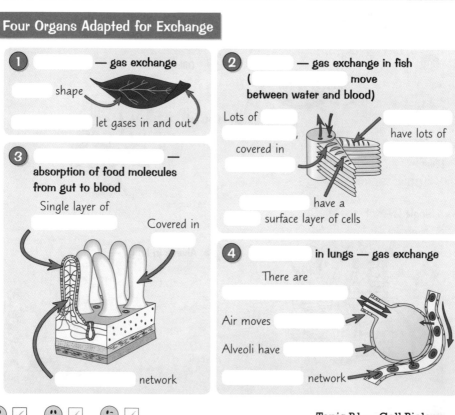

4 [____] in lungs — gas exchange

There are [____]

Air moves [____]

Alveoli have [____]

[____] network

 ☑ ☑ ☑

Exchanging Substances

Surface Area to Volume Ratio

Single-celled organism

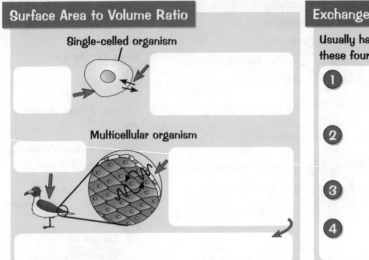

Multicellular organism

Exchange Surfaces

Usually have
these four things:

1

2

3

4

Four Organs Adapted for Exchange

1

in and out

2 Gills —

Lots of

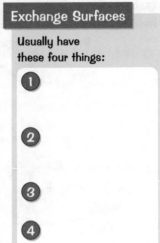

3

Single layer of

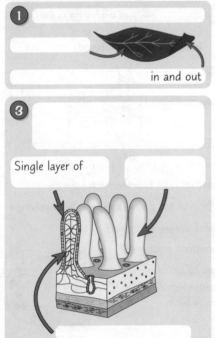

4 Alveoli in lungs —

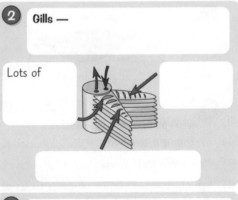

Alveoli

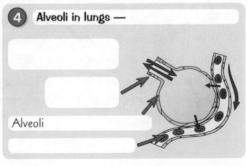

Topic B1 — Cell Biology

Mixed Practice Quizzes

That's your lot for this topic. Before you get carried away with your cell-ebrations, have a go at these quizzes based on p.21-26 to see how much you've learnt.

| Quiz 1 | Date: ...... / ...... / ...... |

1) Give one condition that treatment with stem cells could potentially help.

2) What is active transport?

3) Give two ways leaves are adapted for gas exchange.

4) What is osmosis?

5) Give four ways lungs are adapted for gas exchange.

6) Why do many organisms need exchange surfaces and transport systems?

7) Which process is used to absorb mineral ions from the soil into a plant's root hair cells?

8) Why is it important for an exchange surface to have a thin membrane?

9) What can stem cells from human embryos become?

10) Which organ allows gas exchange in fish?

Total:

| Quiz 2 | Date: ...... / ...... / ...... |

1) What are stem cells?

2) Give a potential risk of using stem cells in medicine.

3) What is diffusion?

4) Why is it important for an exchange surface to have a large surface area?

5) Can stem cells from plant meristems become any kind of plant cell?

6) Which process allows glucose to be absorbed into the bloodstream?

7) Give three ways in which fish gills are adapted for gas exchange.

8) Give two differences between diffusion and active transport.

9) Why do multicellular organisms need transport systems?

10) Which organisms have larger surface area to volume ratios: single-celled organisms or multicellular organisms?

Total:

Mixed Practice Quizzes

Quiz 3 Date: ...... / ...... / ......

1) Does active transport move substances with the concentration gradient or against the concentration gradient?

2) Name three sources of stem cells.

3) Give three factors that increase the rate of diffusion.

4) Give one example of a molecule that can diffuse through a cell membrane.

5) Give three ways in which the small intestine is adapted for absorbing food molecules.

6) Why don't single-celled organisms need exchange surfaces and transport systems?

7) Give two uses of plant stem cells.

8) Does diffusion or osmosis involve the movement of water molecules?

9) True or false? Active transport is the spreading out of particles from an area of higher concentration to an area of lower concentration.

10) True or false? Stem cells can be grown in a lab.

Total:

Quiz 4 Date: ...... / ...... / ......

1) Give one reason why it is useful to be able to produce clones of whole plants quickly and cheaply.

2) In terms of particles, what is meant by a high concentration gradient?

3) True or false? Diffusion requires energy from respiration.

4) True or false? Large and small molecules diffuse through cell membranes.

5) Give four common characteristics of exchange surfaces.

6) True or false? A stem cell taken from adult bone marrow can become any kind of human cell.

7) What type of membrane is involved in osmosis?

8) Stem cells can produce insulin-producing cells to treat what condition?

9) Name the part of a plant that is adapted for gas exchange.

10) Which organ is covered in villi: the small intestine or the lungs?

Total:

Topic B1 — Cell Biology

Cell Organisation and Enzymes

Cell Organisation

_____ — a basic building block that all living organisms have.

↓

TISSUE —

↓

_____ — a group of different _____ that work together.

↓

ORGAN SYSTEM —

Organ systems work together to make entire _____ .

Enzymes

Enzymes _____ (speed up) chemical reactions. Each enzyme only _____ one specific reaction because of the unique shape of its _____ .

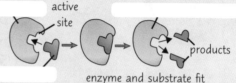

active site

products

enzyme and substrate fit together like _____

_____ temperatures and high and low pHs change the shape of _____ so the enzyme no longer works.

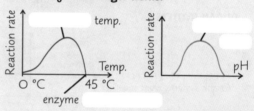

Reaction rate

temp.

Temp.

O °C   45 °C

enzyme _____

Reaction rate

pH

Digestion

_____ break BIG molecules down into smaller, soluble ones. These can pass through the walls of the digestive system and be _____ .

Enzyme	Breaks down...	Into...	Produced in the...
(a carbohydrase)		other sugars	_____ , small intestine,
	protein	acids	_____ , intestine, pancreas
lipase		, fatty acids	_____ , pancreas

The products of digestion can be used to make new _____

Bile speeds up digestion in two ways:

1 It makes conditions _____ so enzymes in the _____ work better.

2 It _____ so there's a larger surface area for _____ to work on.

Bile is made in the _____ and stored in the _____ .

Cell Organisation and Enzymes

Cell Organisation

CELL —

ORGAN SYSTEM —

Organ systems work together to
....

Enzymes

Enzymes

Each enzyme only

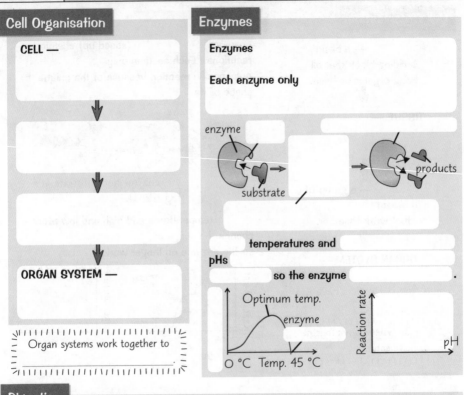

enzyme

substrate

products

temperatures and

pHs

so the enzyme   .

Optimum temp.

enzyme

O °C   Temp. 45 °C

Reaction rate

pH

Digestion

Digestive enzymes

These can pass through

.

Enzyme	Breaks down...	Into...	Produced in the...
amylase (a carbohydrase)			
	protein		
		glycerol, fatty acids	

The .... of digestion can be used ....

Bile is

Bile speeds up digestion in two ways:

1   **2**

 ☑ ☺ ☑

The Lungs and the Heart

The Lungs

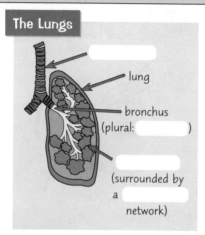

lung

bronchus
(plural:)

(surrounded by
a network)

Gas Exchange

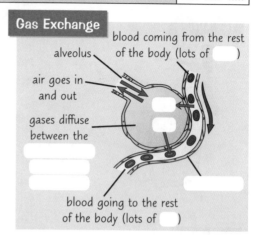

blood coming from the rest
of the body (lots of)

alveolus

air goes in
and out

gases diffuse
between the

blood going to the rest
of the body (lots of)

The Heart

The _____ system is made up of the heart (a pumping organ), blood vessels and blood. Humans have a _____ (two circuits):

Circuit 1 — heart (ventricle) ➡ lungs ⟹

Circuit 2 — heart (ventricle) ⟹ ➡ heart

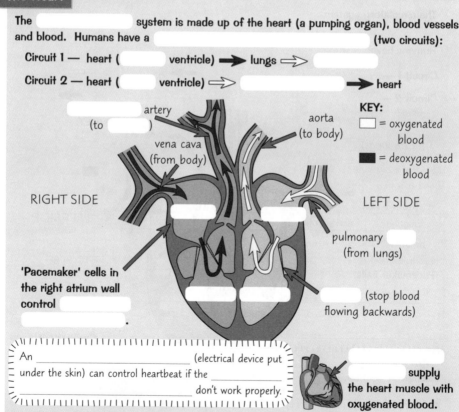

_____ artery
(to)

vena cava
(from body)

aorta
(to body)

RIGHT SIDE

LEFT SIDE

pulmonary
(from lungs)

KEY:
☐ = oxygenated
blood

■ = deoxygenated
blood

'Pacemaker' cells in
the right atrium wall
control _____
_____.

(stop blood
flowing backwards)

An _____ (electrical device put
under the skin) can control heartbeat if the _____
_____ don't work properly.

_____ supply
the heart muscle with
oxygenated blood.

The Lungs and the Heart

The Lungs

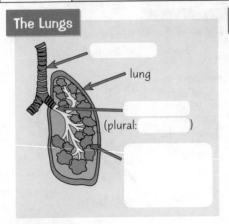

lung

(plural:)

Gas Exchange

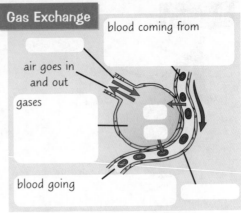

blood coming from

air goes in
and out

gases

blood going

The Heart

The circulatory system

Humans have

Circuit 1 —

Circuit 2 —

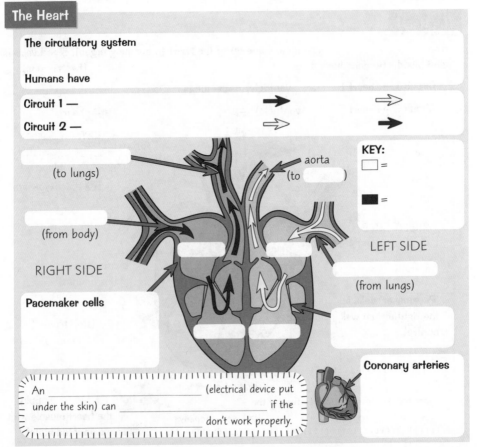

(to lungs)

aorta

(to)

(from body)

KEY:

☐ =

■ =

RIGHT SIDE

LEFT SIDE

(from lungs)

Pacemaker cells

Coronary arteries

An _____ (electrical device put
under the skin) can _____ if the
_____ don't work properly.

Blood Vessels and Blood

Three Types of Blood Vessel

1 _____ carry blood away from the heart.

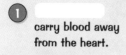

thick muscle and elastic layers because blood pressure is _____

2 _____ carry blood close to body cells to exchange substances.

thin, _____ walls to allow substances to _____ in and out easily

3 _____ carry blood back to the heart.

_____ inside stop blood flowing backwards

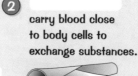

thinner walls than _____ because blood pressure is _____

$$\text{rate of blood flow} = \frac{\text{volume of blood}}{\text{..................}}$$

Four Blood Components

Blood is a _____.

Component	Function	Description
1 _____ blood cells	Carry _____ around the body.	no _____ so more room for _____ _____ shape = big surface area = lots of _____ absorbed contains _____, which binds to _____
2 _____ blood cells	Defend against _____.	phagocytosis antitoxins _____
3 Platelets	Help blood to _____.	fragments of _____
4 _____	Carries _____ in the blood.	hormones amino acids red blood cells urea glucose antibodies antitoxins white blood cells liquid proteins platelets CO_2

Blood Vessels and Blood

Three Types of Blood Vessel

1 Arteries

2 Capillaries

3 _____

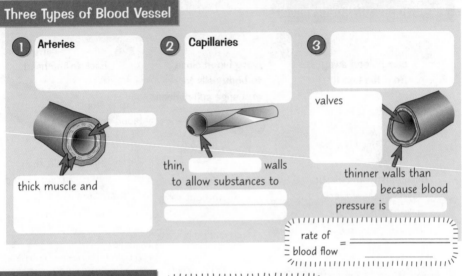

valves

thick muscle and

thin, _____ walls
to allow substances to

thinner walls than
_____ because blood
pressure is _____

$$\text{rate of blood flow} = \frac{\rule{2cm}{0.4pt}}{\rule{2cm}{0.4pt}}$$

Four Blood Components

Component	Function	Description
1		no _____ so more room for _____ contains _____ ・ _____ = big surface area = _____
2		_____ → _____ → _____ → _____
3 Platelets		_____ →
4		hormones, amino acids, urea, glucose, antibodies, antitoxins, proteins, _____ CO_2

 ☑ ☑ ☑

Cardiovascular Disease

Coronary Heart Disease

[blank] — diseases of the heart or blood vessels,
e.g. coronary heart disease:

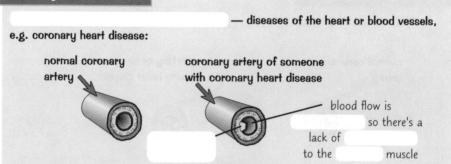

normal coronary
artery

coronary artery of someone
with coronary heart disease

blood flow is [blank] so there's a
lack of [blank]
to the [blank] muscle

Five Treatments for Cardiovascular Disease

Treatment	Advantages	Disadvantages
1 Statins	[blank] the amount of LDL cholesterol in the blood, which slows down the formation of [blank] [blank].	• Need to be taken long-term. • Can have [blank] [blank].
2 [blank] (tube put in coronary artery) fatty deposit squashed	• Keeps coronary arteries open for a long time. • [blank] [blank] is pretty quick.	• [blank] can cause bleeding and infection.
3 [blank] (heart from a donor)	• Can treat heart failure. • Donor hearts work better than [blank] [blank].	• Donor hearts or valves can be [blank] [blank].
4 [blank]	Can be used while waiting for a donor heart or while the heart is [blank].	• Artificial devices can lead to [blank] (blood clots in blood vessels).
5 Replacement heart valves — [blank] or [blank]	Can treat severe valve damage (e.g. stiff valves that don't open properly or [blank]).	Faulty heart valves stop

Cardiovascular Disease

Coronary Heart Disease

CARDIOVASCULAR DISEASES —

normal coronary artery

coronary artery of someone with coronary heart disease

Five Treatments for Cardiovascular Disease

Treatment	Advantages	Disadvantages
① Statins	Reduce the amount of	• •
②	• Keeps coronary arteries •	• Surgery can • Donor hearts or valves can
③ (heart from a donor)	• •	
④ Artificial heart		• Artificial devices can
⑤		Faulty heart valves _____ _____ _____

Mixed Practice Quizzes

I know you've been turning every page excitedly wondering when the next quizzes were coming... well, the wait is over — time to test yourself on p.29-36.

Quiz 1 | Date: ...... / ...... / ......

1) Where in the heart are pacemaker cells found?
2) Define 'organ'.
3) Which enzyme breaks down starch?
4) Which side of the heart receives blood from the lungs?
5) How do stents work as a treatment for coronary heart disease?
6) Why do capillaries have thin, permeable walls?
7) What is the liquid component of blood called?
8) Why is each enzyme only able to catalyse one specific reaction?
9) Name the structures in the lungs where gas exchange takes place.
10) What is the role of digestive enzymes?

Total:

Quiz 2 | Date: ...... / ...... / ......

1) Where is bile made? Where is it stored?
2) Which blood vessels supply the heart muscle with oxygenated blood?
3) How do statins help people with cardiovascular diseases?
4) Why don't enzymes work at high temperatures?
5) What does an artificial pacemaker do?
6) Give three places in the body where protease is produced.
7) Explain why there is a lack of oxygen reaching the heart muscle in people with coronary heart disease.
8) How does the structure of arteries make them suited to their function?
9) What do platelets do?
10) Give two advantages of heart transplants.

Total:

Mixed Practice Quizzes

Quiz 3   Date: ...... / ...... / ......

1) Why is the term 'lock and key' used to describe enzyme action?
2) What is the name for the two tubes that the trachea splits into, one of which goes into each lung?
3) Give three examples of things carried in the plasma.
4) What does lipase break lipids down into?
5) List three ways that white blood cells defend against infection.
6) Give two disadvantages of using statins to treat cardiovascular diseases.
7) Which digestive enzyme is produced in the salivary glands, small intestine and pancreas?
8) Describe the role of the pulmonary artery.
9) Which type of blood vessel has valves inside?
10) How does the shape of red blood cells make them adapted for carrying oxygen around the body?

Total:

Quiz 4   Date: ...... / ...... / ......

1) What term describes a group of organs that work together?
2) What is the role of the aorta?
3) Why do arteries have thicker walls than veins?
4) Describe the movement of gases between alveoli and the capillaries that surround them.
5) Define 'tissue'.
6) Which chamber of the heart pumps blood to the lungs?
7) Explain two ways in which bile speeds up digestion.
8) Explain what happens to an enzyme's activity at extreme pHs.
9) Give two possible problems with heart valves that could lead to a person needing replacement valves.
10) Give one disadvantage of donor hearts and valves.

Total:

Health and Disease

Health

HEALTH —

_____ can cause ill health.

These three things can also affect health:

1 _____

2 stress

3 life situation, e.g. _____

Two Types of Disease

1 COMMUNICABLE DISEASE —
a disease that can spread from
_____ or
between _____
_____ .

2 NON-COMMUNICABLE
DISEASE —

Four Ways That Diseases May Interact

	Initial problem	Issue that can be made more likely
1	disorder affecting immune system	_____ diseases
2	infection by certain _____	certain cancers
3	pathogen infection that causes _____	_____ (e.g. rashes or asthma)
4	severe physical health problems	mental health issues (e.g. _____)

Cost of Non-Communicable Diseases

Human cost —

_____ of
people die from non-communicable
diseases each _____ .

Those living with these diseases may
have a poorer quality of life and
_____ .

Financial cost —

_____
_____
costs health organisations
(e.g. the NHS) loads of money.

Those with diseases may not be
able to work, which can affect
_____ as well as
the _____ .

Health and Disease

Health

HEALTH —

[ ] can cause ill health.

These three things can also affect health:

1. [ ]

2. [ ]

3. [ ]

Two Types of Disease

1. COMMUNICABLE DISEASE —

2. [ ]

Four Ways That Diseases May Interact

	Initial problem	Issue that can be made more likely
1	disorder affecting [ ]	[ ] diseases
2	infection by [ ]	certain [ ]
3		
4	severe [ ] [ ] problems	

Cost of Non-Communicable Diseases

Human cost —

Financial cost —

Those living with

Those with diseases

Risk Factors for Diseases and Cancer

Five Risk Factors for Non-Communicable Diseases

RISK FACTORS —

1 A lack of [ ] and an unhealthy (e.g. [ ])
diet are linked to cardiovascular disease.

2 Obesity is linked to Type [ ] diabetes and
cancer of the bowel, liver and [ ].

3 Drinking too much alcohol can cause [ ]
disease and affect [ ] function.

[ ] or
[ ]
while pregnant
can cause health problems for
the unborn baby.

4 Smoking can cause [ ]
disease, lung disease and lung cancer. It is also linked to
mouth, bowel, [ ] and [ ] cancer.

5 Exposure to [ ]
(e.g. ionising radiation) can cause [ ].

Many non-communicable diseases are caused by several risk factors [ ].

Cancer

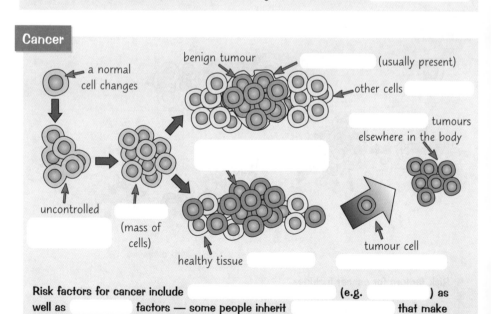

a normal
cell changes

benign tumour

[ ] (usually present)

other cells [ ]

[ ] tumours
elsewhere in the body

uncontrolled

[ ]

[ ]

(mass of
cells)

healthy tissue [ ]

tumour cell

[ ]

Risk factors for cancer include [ ] (e.g. [ ]) as
well as [ ] factors — some people inherit [ ] that make
them more susceptible to cancer.

Risk Factors for Diseases and Cancer

Five Risk Factors for Non-Communicable Diseases

RISK FACTORS —

1. _____ are linked to cardiovascular disease.

2. Obesity is linked to

3. Drinking too much alcohol can cause

_____ while pregnant can cause _____.

4. Smoking

5. Exposure to _____ can cause cancer.

Many non-communicable diseases are

Cancer

Risk factors for cancer include

Plant Cell Organisation

Six Plant Tissues

1 Epidermal tissue — covered with a _____ in the leaf to reduce water loss. Cells in the upper layer are transparent to let _____ .

2 Palisade mesophyll tissue — where most _____ happens (so there are lots of _____).

3 _____ tissue — has air spaces to allow the _____ of gases.

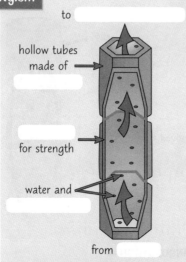

4 Xylem

5 _____

lower epidermal layer

Leaves are _____ . Together with the roots and stem they form an _____ that _____ substances around the plant.

6 Meristem tissue — found at the _____ . The cells can _____ into many types of cell so the plant can grow.

Xylem

to _____

hollow tubes made of _____

_____ for strength

water and _____

from _____

Xylem tissue carries water in the _____ .

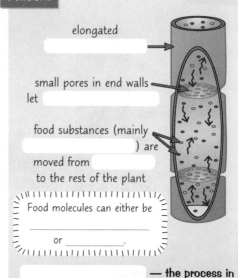

Phloem

elongated _____

small pores in end walls let _____

food substances (mainly _____) are moved from _____ to the rest of the plant

Food molecules can either be _____ or _____ .

_____ — the process in which food is moved through phloem tubes.

Plant Cell Organisation

Six Plant Tissues

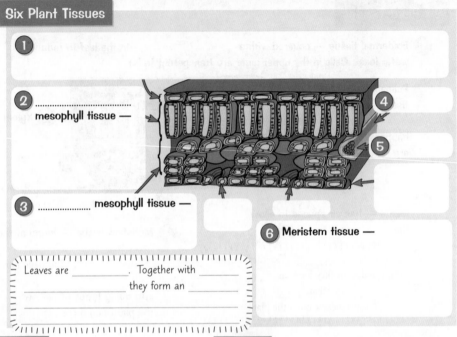

1

2 ....
mesophyll tissue —

3 .... mesophyll tissue —

4

5

6 Meristem tissue —

Leaves are .... Together with ....
they form an ....
....
....

Xylem

to ....

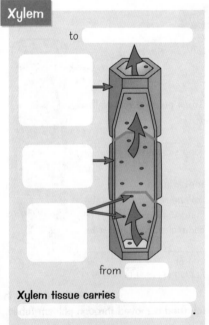

from ....

Xylem tissue carries ....
....

Phloem

.... cells

....

.... are moved from ....

....

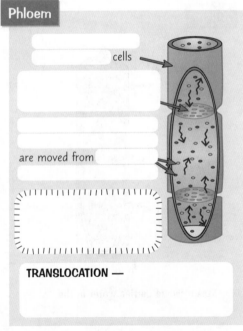

TRANSLOCATION —

Topic B2 — Organisation

Transpiration

Transpiration Basics

TRANSPIRATION —

Water ⬜ and ⬜
out of the plant...

...which causes

Transpiration Rate

These four things ⬜
transpiration rate:

1 Warm temperatures

Water molecules have
⬜.

2 ⬜ light intensity

⬜ when it's light.

3 ⬜
air flow

4 Low ⬜

⬜ water molecules
surround the leaves (so there's
a ⬜
⬜
inside the leaf than outside it).

Guard Cells and Stomata

Guard cells are adapted for
⬜ and controlling ⬜
⬜.

When the plant has lots of water...

⬜ ⬜

guard
cells

OPEN

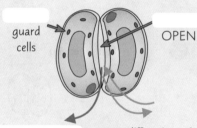

⬜ gases diffuse in and
escapes out (e.g. ⬜ for ⬜)

When the plant is short of
water or ⬜ ...

⬜

guard
cells

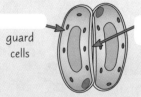

Transpiration

Transpiration Basics

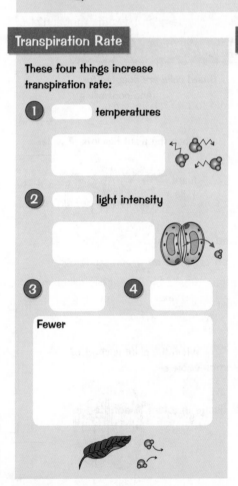

TRANSPIRATION —

Transpiration Rate

These four things increase transpiration rate:

1. temperatures

2. light intensity

3.   4.

Fewer

Guard Cells and Stomata

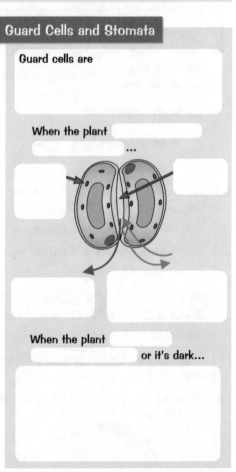

Guard cells are

When the plant

...

When the plant

or it's dark...

Topic B2 — Organisation

Mixed Practice Quizzes

Well, here we are again. All sorts of stuff was covered over pages 39-46 —
have a go at these quizzes to see how much of it has stuck in your head.

Quiz 1   Date: ...... / ...... / ......

1) What happens to stomata when a plant is in darkness?
2) What is meant by a 'non-communicable' disease?
3) What is phloem tissue made up of?
4) What type of non-communicable disease can be caused by exposure to carcinogens?
5) Describe how water is lost from a plant.
6) How is the structure of spongy mesophyll tissue adapted to its function?
7) True or false? Malignant tumours can form secondary tumours.
8) Other than diseases, name three things that can affect health.
9) What type of cells surround stomata?
10) True or false? Physical illnesses can lead to mental illnesses.

Total:

Quiz 2   Date: ...... / ...... / ......

1) What is the term for a disease that can spread from person to person or between animals and people?
2) List three health problems that are linked to smoking.
3) Which term describes a leaf: a tissue, an organ or an organ system?
4) Under what conditions would a plant's guard cells be flaccid?
5) Give three risk factors for cardiovascular disease.
6) Describe the function of phloem tissue.
7) Which tissue in a leaf is where most photosynthesis happens?
8) Describe two human costs of non-communicable diseases.
9) Describe how a tumour forms.
10) Describe two ways in which epidermal tissue in a leaf is adapted to its function.

Total:

Topic B2 — Organisation

Mixed Practice Quizzes

Date: ...... / ...... / ......

1) Define 'health'.
2) Give two differences between a benign tumour and a malignant tumour.
3) Describe where meristem tissue is found in a plant.
4) How does the level of humidity affect a plant's transpiration rate?
5) Give two possible health consequences of drinking too much alcohol.
6) Give two examples of allergic reactions that can be triggered by a pathogen infection.
7) What is transpiration?
8) What strengthens the hollow tubes that make up xylem tissue?
9) How can non-communicable diseases have a financial cost on families and the national economy?
10) Describe a risk factor for cancer that is not a lifestyle factor.

Total:

Quiz 4   Date: ...... / ...... / ......

1) What is meant by a 'risk factor' for a non-communicable disease?
2) How are secondary tumours formed?
3) Give one way that a person's life situation might affect their health.
4) What is translocation?
5) How is palisade mesophyll tissue adapted for its function?
6) Name one disease that is linked to obesity.
7) Describe how temperature affects a plant's transpiration rate.
8) What is the function of xylem tissue?
9) What is another health problem that can be triggered by infection by certain viruses?
10) True or false? Guard cells help to control gas exchange in a plant.

Total:

Communicable Disease

First Go:
..... / ..... / .....

Infectious Diseases

PATHOGENS — microorganisms that cause _____ which _____ between organisms.

Disease	Pathogen	How it's spread	Symptoms	Prevention / treatment
Rose black spot		• Water • _____	• _____ spots on leaves, can turn yellow and _____ • Reduced growth	• Removing and destroying infected leaves • _____
Malaria		_____ vectors	• _____ • Can be _____	• Stop mosquitoes from _____
_____ food poisoning	Bacterium	Eating _____	• Fever • _____ • Vomiting • _____	• Vaccination of _____ • _____ food preparation
Gonorrhoea		Sexual contact	• Pain when _____ • _____ discharge from vagina or penis	• _____ • Antibiotics
_____	Virus	_____ (coughs and sneezes)	• _____ • _____ skin rash • Can be _____	Vaccination of _____
HIV		• Sexual contact • _____ (e.g. blood)	• Flu-like (initially) • A damaged _____ (late stage infection/AIDS)	• _____ • Avoid sharing _____ • _____
_____ virus (TMV)	Virus		_____ on leaves, which reduces _____ and growth	

Second Go:
...... /...... /......

Communicable Disease

Infectious Diseases

PATHOGENS — microorganisms that

Disease	Pathogen	How it's spread	Symptoms	Prevention / treatment
Rose black spot	• •		• •	• Removing and •
Malaria			• •	• •
	Bacterium		• • Stomach cramps • •	• Vaccination of •
Gonorrhoea			• •	• •
	Virus		• • Red skin rash •	
HIV	• •		• •	• • •
	Virus		Mosaic pattern	

Topic B3 — Infection and Response

Fighting Disease

Four Non-Specific Defence Systems Against Pathogens

1 Skin — acts as a [____] and secretes [____] substances to kill pathogens.

2 Nose — [____] and [____] trap particles containing [____].

3 Trachea and bronchi — mucus [____] pathogens, and [____] waft mucus up to the [____] so that it can be [____].

4 Stomach — [____] [____] kills pathogens.

Three Ways White Blood Cells Attack Pathogens

1 Phagocytosis

[____] engulfed and digested

2 Producing [____]

pathogen with [____]   antibodies [____] to pathogen produced

antibodies [____] all copies of the pathogen in the body

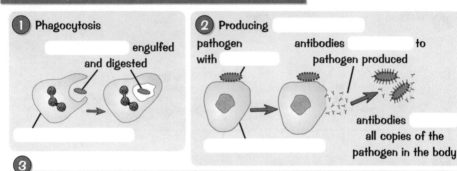

3 Producing [____] — these counteract toxins produced by invading [____].

Vaccination

Vaccinating a [____] of the population greatly [____] the spread of pathogens so that even people who aren't vaccinated are [____] to catch the disease.

[____]

pathogens

needle

[____]

[____] produced

If [____] pathogens of the [____] try to attack...

... so you [____].

... they are quickly [____] and attacked by [____] ...

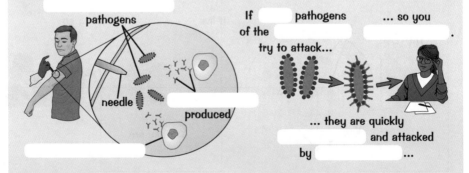

Topic B3 — Infection and Response

Fighting Disease

Four Non-Specific Defence Systems Against Pathogens

1 Skin —

2 Nose —

3 Trachea and bronchi —

4 Stomach —

Three Ways White Blood Cells Attack Pathogens

1

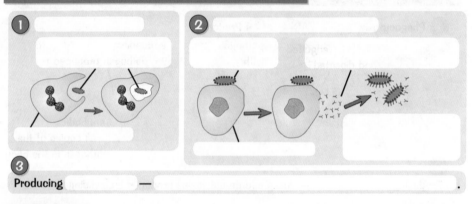

2

3 Producing _____ — _____ .

Vaccination

Vaccinating a _____
the spread of pathogens so that _____
_____ .

If live _____

... so _____ .

...

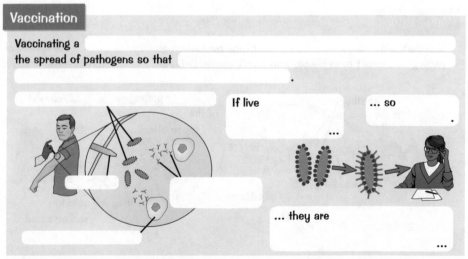

... they are _____

...

Drugs

First Go:
..... / ..... / .....

Types of Drugs

Antibiotics kill [ ] .

[ ] antibiotics kill types of [ ] .

Use of [ ] Deaths from [ ]
Time

It's hard to [ ] that destroy [ ] because they live and reproduce inside [ ] .

Painkillers treat the [ ] of disease but don't kill [ ] .

Where Drugs Come From

Drug	Type	Source
Digitalis	Heart drug	
	Painkiller	
		Penicillium mould

Nowadays, drugs [ ] [ ] in a lab, but the process still might start with a [ ] [ ] extracted from a [ ] .

[ ] was discovered by Alexander Fleming.

Drug Testing

New drugs are [ ] to check they're [ ] .
They are tested for three things:

1 [ ] — how harmful the drug is.

2 Efficacy — whether the drug [ ] and produces the [ ] you're looking for.

3 Dosage — the [ ] that should be given, and [ ] it should be given.

Preclinical Testing

Tests on [ ] and tissues ➔ Tests on [ ] ➔

Clinical trials are often [ ]

Given drug

Given placebo

Clinical Trials

Tests on [ ]
The dosage is gradually [ ] from a [ ] dose

Tests on [ ]
Finding [ ] dose

PLACEBOS — substances that [ ]
[ ] .

 ☑ ☑   ☑

Topic B3 — Infection and Response

Second Go:
..... /..... /.....

Drugs

Types of Drugs

Antibiotics _____ .

_____

_____

Time

It's hard to

Painkillers

Where Drugs Come From

Drug	Type	Source

Nowadays,

_____ was discovered by _____

Drug Testing

New drugs are _____ .
They are tested for three things:

1

2

3

_____

Tests on ____ → **Tests on** ____ → **Tests on** ____

_____

_____

Tests on ____

_____

PLACEBOS —

Mixed Practice Quizzes

Time for more quizzes. Let's see what you've picked up from p.49-54 — knowledge, I mean, not diseases. Mark your answers when you're done.

Quiz 1 | Date: ...... / ...... / ......

1) List three things that new drugs are tested on during preclinical tests.
2) What type of pathogen causes rose black spot?
3) How is measles spread?
4) Why is it hard to develop drugs that destroy viruses?
5) Explain how getting vaccinated against a disease protects you from getting that disease in the future.
6) Give one symptom of malaria.
7) What type of drugs are used to treat HIV?
8) Give four non-specific defence systems present in humans.
9) What happens to the leaves of plants infected by rose black spot?
10) What organism is the source of aspirin?

Total:

Quiz 2 | Date: ...... / ...... / ......

1) How are the pathogens given in vaccinations different to those that people might encounter normally?
2) Describe what happens during phagocytosis.
3) How is gonorrhoea spread?
4) How does the dosage of drugs given change during clinical trials?
5) How has the increased use of antibiotics affected the number of deaths from bacterial disease?
6) Give two symptoms of measles.
7) How does the skin defend against pathogens?
8) List four symptoms of *Salmonella* food poisoning.
9) What type of pathogen causes: a) HIV? b) malaria?
10) What is the purpose of antitoxins?

Total:

Topic B3 — Infection and Response

Mixed Practice Quizzes

Quiz 3 Date: ...... / ...... / ......

1) Give two ways in which the spread of malaria can be prevented.
2) Describe the symptoms of tobacco mosaic virus.
3) How is rose black spot spread?
4) How do people get *Salmonella* food poisoning?
5) What are scientists looking for when testing the efficacy of a new drug?
6) What type of drug is digitalis?
7) What is a pathogen?
8) How do the trachea and bronchi defend against pathogens?
9) a) Give two symptoms of gonorrhoea.
   b) How can gonorrhoea be treated?
10) Who discovered penicillin?

Total:

Quiz 4 Date: ...... / ...... / ......

1) Which of these diseases is caused by a bacterium:
   measles, malaria or gonorrhoea?
2) Give two ways in which HIV is spread.
3) Which condition results from a late stage HIV infection?
4) What is meant by a 'double-blind' drugs trial?
5) How does vaccinating a large proportion of a population help to protect
   those who aren't vaccinated from getting a disease?
6) What type of microorganisms do antibiotics kill?
7) Give three ways in which white blood cells attack pathogens.
8) How does the nose defend against pathogens?
9) Give two ways in which the spread of rose black spot can be prevented.
10) What is a placebo?

Total:

Photosynthesis

The Photosynthesis Reaction

PHOTOSYNTHESIS — an _____ reaction in which _____
is transferred to chloroplasts from the environment by _____ .

_____ + water ⟶ glucose + _____

6CO₂   6H₂O   6O₂

Four Uses of Glucose in Plants

1. _____ — energy is transferred from glucose.

2. Strengthening cell walls — glucose is converted into _____ ,
which is used to make strong cell walls.

3. Protein synthesis — glucose and _____ are used to
make _____ , which are then made into proteins.

4. Energy storage — glucose is turned into _____ or _____
_____ to store energy.

Rate of Photosynthesis

An _____ in any of these four factors tends
to increase the _____ of photosynthesis:

1. _____
2. _____

3. CO₂ concentration
4. Amount of chlorophyll

Any of these factors can become the limiting factor (_____
_____).

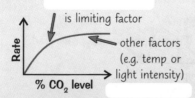

_____ is limiting factor

Rate

other factors
(e.g. temp or
light intensity)

% CO₂ level _____

temperature is
limiting factor

Rate

high temperatures
_____

involved in
photosynthesis

Temperature (°C)

Second Go:
..... / ..... / .....

Photosynthesis

The Photosynthesis Reaction

PHOTOSYNTHESIS — an [_____] in which [_____]

[_____] by light.

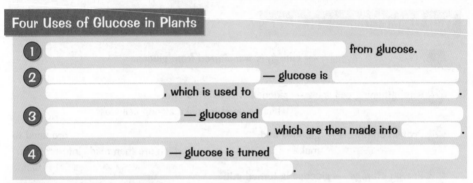

[........................]   +   [................]   →   [................]   +   [................]

[........................] $6H_2O$ [................]   [................]

Four Uses of Glucose in Plants

① [_____] from glucose.

② [_____] — glucose is [_____]

[_____], which is used to [_____].

③ [_____] — glucose and [_____]

[_____], which are then made into [_____].

④ [_____] — glucose is turned [_____]

[_____].

Rate of Photosynthesis

An increase [_____]

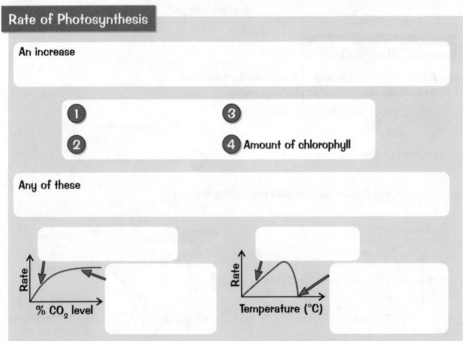

① [_____]   ③ [_____]

② [_____]   ④ Amount of chlorophyll

Any of these [_____]

Rate vs % CO_2 level

Rate vs Temperature (°C)

Respiration

Energy Transfer

RESPIRATION — the process of transferring energy [_____].
It's an [_____] reaction that goes on continuously in [_____].

The energy transferred is used [_____].
Three examples of these are:

1 To [_____] for movement.

2 To keep warm (in [_____]).

3 To build up [_____] molecules from [_____].

Aerobic Respiration

AEROBIC RESPIRATION —
respiration using [_____].   [____] + oxygen ⟶ [____] + water

It's the most [_____]
type of respiration. $C_6H_{12}O_6$ [____] $6CO_2$ [____]

Anaerobic Respiration

ANAEROBIC RESPIRATION — respiration [_____].

It transfers [_____] than [_____] respiration
because glucose isn't fully [_____].

In muscle cells: In plant and yeast cells:

glucose ⟶ [_____]   glucose ⟶ ethanol + [_____]

In yeast cells, anaerobic respiration is called [_____].
The process is used to make [_____]

Topic B4 — Bioenergetics

Respiration

Energy Transfer

RESPIRATION —

It's an

The energy _____ .
Three examples of these are:

1 _____

2 _____

3 _____

Aerobic Respiration

AEROBIC RESPIRATION —

It's the

```
.............. + ..............  ➡  .............. + ..............
                6O₂                  ..............   ..............
```

$$\text{..............} + \text{..............} \rightarrow \text{..............} + \text{..............}$$
$$6O_2$$

Anaerobic Respiration

ANAEROBIC RESPIRATION —
It transfers

In _____ cells: In plant and _____

_____ ➡ _____   _____ ➡ _____ + _____

In

The process is used to

Metabolism and Exercise

Metabolism

METABOLISM — the sum of all the [_____] that happen

in [_____].

Metabolic reactions use [_____]
to make new molecules, e.g.:

[_____] and nitrate
ions combined to make
amino acids, then [_____].

Lipids broken down
into [_____]

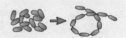

[_____]
joined together to make
bigger [_____]
(e.g. [_____] or glycogen).

Effects of Exercise on the Body

EXERCISE

⬇

more .... needed

⬇

more ....
.... needed

⬇

more .... needed

These three things [_____] to
get more [_____] to your muscles:

 Heart rate

 [_____] rate

 [_____]

.... also cause muscle fatigue
— the muscles get tired and ....
....

Oxygen Debt

OXYGEN DEBT — [_____]
oxygen your body needs
[_____].

During [_____],
not enough oxygen is supplied to
the muscles so:

[_____]
takes place in muscles

⬇

Lactic acid [_____]

⬇

[_____]
created

⬇

[_____] and breathing
rate stay high after exercise
to repay oxygen debt

Metabolism and Exercise

Metabolism

METABOLISM —

Metabolic reactions use

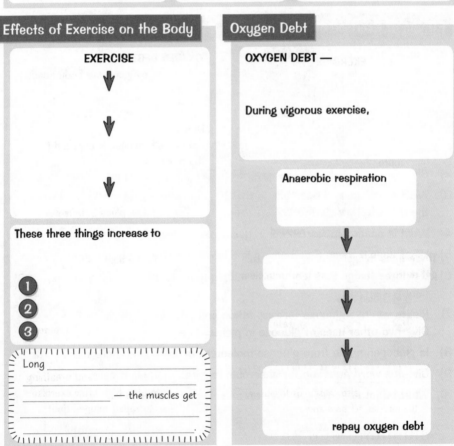

Effects of Exercise on the Body

EXERCISE

These three things increase to

1
2
3

Long _____

_____ — the muscles get

_____

Oxygen Debt

OXYGEN DEBT —

During vigorous exercise,

Anaerobic respiration

repay oxygen debt

Mixed Practice Quizzes

All that talk of exercise is enough to make me feel out of breath, but we've made it to the end of the topic already — phew. Time to test yourself on p.57-62.

Quiz 1 | Date: ...... / ...... / ......

1) True or false? Photosynthesis is an endothermic reaction.
2) What is respiration?
3) List four factors that tend to increase the rate of photosynthesis.
4) Which type of respiration is more efficient, aerobic or anaerobic?
5) Give two things that plants convert glucose to for storage.
6) Which type of respiration doesn't use oxygen?
7) What are lipids broken down into?
8) What are the products of anaerobic respiration in yeast cells?
9) In plants, what is needed in addition to glucose to make proteins?
10) Explain how exercise affects the body's need for oxygen.

Total:

Quiz 2 | Date: ...... / ...... / ......

1) Give the word equation for aerobic respiration.
2) Give three processes that energy transferred by respiration is used for.
3) What effect does a decrease in the CO_2 concentration tend to have on the rate of photosynthesis?
4) What is anaerobic respiration in yeast cells called?
5) What does it mean if something is a limiting factor of photosynthesis?
6) List three things that increase to supply more oxygen to the muscles during exercise.
7) Plants can use glucose for respiration and protein synthesis. Give two other uses of glucose in plants.
8) Is glycogen made from glucose molecules or fatty acid molecules?
9) Give the word equation for anaerobic respiration in plant cells.
10) What effect does fatigue have on muscle contraction?

Total:

Mixed Practice Quizzes

Quiz 3   Date: ...... / ...... / ......

1) During photosynthesis, energy is transferred from the environment to which subcellular structure?
2) Is respiration an endothermic or exothermic reaction?
3) Which process transfers energy from glucose?
4) Give the word equation for photosynthesis.
5) What effect does an increase in light intensity tend to have on the rate of photosynthesis?
6) What are the products of aerobic respiration?
7) Explain why an oxygen debt is created during vigorous exercise.
8) True or false? Anaerobic respiration in muscle cells produces lactic acid.
9) Give four uses of glucose in plants.
10) What molecule is represented by the chemical formula $C_6H_{12}O_6$?

Total:

Quiz 4   Date: ...... / ...... / ......

1) True or false? Photosynthesis requires light.
2) Why does anaerobic respiration transfer less energy than aerobic respiration?
3) Give an example of a food product that fermentation is used to make.
4) Define 'metabolism'.
5) Why does breath volume increase during exercise?
6) Why does photosynthesis stop at high temperatures?
7) What process is represented by this equation:
   $6CO_2 + 6H_2O \rightarrow C_6H_{12}O_6 + 6O_2$?
8) What is meant by oxygen debt?
9) How do plants use glucose to strengthen their cell walls?
10) Give one example of how energy from respiration is used to make new molecules.

Total:

Homeostasis and the Nervous System

Maintaining a Stable Internal Environment

HOMEOSTASIS — the [_____] inside your [_____]. It maintains a stable internal environment in response to changes in [_____] conditions.

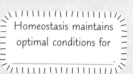
Homeostasis maintains optimal conditions for [_____]

Component of control systems	Function of component
Receptors	To detect [_____] (changes in [_____])
[_____]	To [_____] and [_____] information from receptors and organise a [_____]
Effectors	To produce a response to [_____] and restore [_____]

Automatic control systems can involve [_____] or [_____] responses.

Three things in your body that are [_____] by control systems:

 [_____]   [_____]   [_____]

The Nervous System

NEURONES — cells that [_____] as [_____] in the nervous system. The nervous system means that humans can [_____] and [_____].

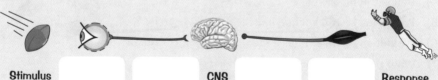

Stimulus [_____] [_____] CNS [_____] [_____] Response

CENTRAL NERVOUS SYSTEM (CNS) — consists of the [_____] and [_____]. It is connected to the body by [_____] neurones and [_____] neurones.

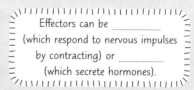
Effectors can be [_____] (which respond to nervous impulses by contracting) or [_____] (which secrete hormones).

Homeostasis and the Nervous System

Maintaining a Stable Internal Environment

HOMEOSTASIS —

Homeostasis maintains
_____
_____

Component of control systems	Function of component
Receptors	
	To _____ from receptors
Effectors	

_____ can involve _____ or _____ responses.

Three things in your body that are _____ :

1 _____ 2 _____ 3 _____

The Nervous System

NEURONES — cells that _____
_____ . The nervous system means that humans can
_____ .

CENTRAL NERVOUS SYSTEM (CNS) —

It is

Effectors can be _____ (which
_____
_____) or _____
(which _____).

Synapses, Reflexes and Hormones

Synapses

SYNAPSE — the [   ]
between two [   ].
A nerve signal is transferred
across a [   ] by the
[   ].

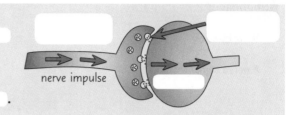

nerve impulse

Reflex Arcs

REFLEXES — [   ], [   ] responses to certain [   ] that don't involve
the [   ]. They can reduce the chance of [   ].

Five steps in a reflex arc:

1	Stimulation of ....
2	Impulses travel along ....
3	Impulses passed along ....
4	Impulses travel along ....
5	.... contracts and arm moves

The Endocrine System

ENDOCRINE SYSTEM — made up
of [   ] that secrete chemicals
(known as [   ]) directly into
the [   ], which carries
them to the [   ].

[   ] (male)
produce testosterone

The effects of hormones
are .... than nerves
but last ....

'master gland',
stimulates other glands

produces thyroxine

produces adrenaline

produces insulin

[   ] (female)
produce oestrogen

 ✓   ✓   ✓

Topic B5 — Homeostasis and Response

Synapses, Reflexes and Hormones

Synapses

SYNAPSE —

A nerve signal

Reflex Arcs

REFLEXES — _____ that don't involve
the _____. They can _____.

Five steps in a _____ :

1	
2	
3	
4	
5	

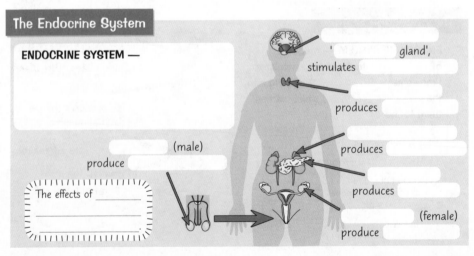

The Endocrine System

ENDOCRINE SYSTEM —

' _____ gland',
stimulates _____

produces _____

_____ (male)
produce _____

produces _____

produces _____

The effects of _____
_____

produces _____

_____ (female)
produce _____

Topic B5 — Homeostasis and Response

Blood Glucose, Diabetes and Puberty

Controlling Blood Glucose

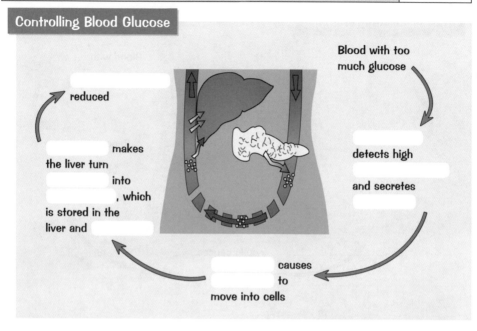

Blood with too much glucose

reduced

_____ makes the liver turn _____ into _____ , which is stored in the liver and _____

detects high _____ and secretes _____

_____ causes _____ to move into cells

Diabetes

	Type 1	Type 2
Cause	Pancreas produces _____ insulin	_____ no longer respond to _____ properly
Effect	_____ rise to _____ levels	
Treatment	Insulin	controlled diet and regular _____

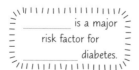

_____ is a major risk factor for _____ diabetes.

Puberty and Sex Hormones

PUBERTY — when the body starts releasing _____ , which trigger the development of _____ (e.g. facial hair in men and breasts in women).

In men, the main reproductive hormone is _____ , which stimulates _____ .

In women, the main reproductive hormone is _____ .

Topic B5 — Homeostasis and Response

Blood Glucose, Diabetes and Puberty

Controlling Blood Glucose

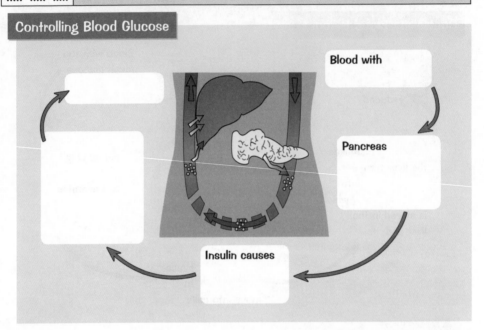

Blood with

Pancreas

Insulin causes

Diabetes

	Type 1	Type 2
Cause		
Effect		
Treatment		and

Puberty and Sex Hormones

PUBERTY — when the

which

(e.g. facial hair
in men and breasts in women).

In men,

In women,

The Menstrual Cycle & Contraception

Stages of the Menstrual Cycle

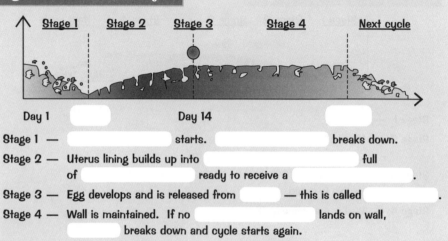

Stage 1   Stage 2   Stage 3   Stage 4   Next cycle

Day 1   Day 14

Stage 1 — _____ starts. _____ breaks down.

Stage 2 — Uterus lining builds up into _____ full of _____ ready to receive a _____ .

Stage 3 — Egg develops and is released from ____ — this is called _____ .

Stage 4 — Wall is maintained. If no _____ lands on wall, ____ breaks down and cycle starts again.

Four Hormones That Control the Menstrual Cycle

1 FSH (_____) — causes an ____ to mature in an ____ .

2 _____ causes uterus lining to grow.

3 LH (_____) — stimulates ovulation.

4 _____ maintains uterus lining.

Contraception

CONTRACEPTION — methods of ____ the likelihood of ____ reaching an ovulated egg.

Hormonal methods	Non-hormonal methods
Oral contraceptive pills contain _____ that inhibit ____ and stop _____ .	_____ and _____ physically prevent sperm from reaching egg.
The contraceptive implant releases _____ continuously to stop _____ and _____ of eggs.	Sterilisation — a _____ surgical procedure to stop a man or woman from _____ .
Injections or _____ work in a similar way to implants but _____ .	_____ disable or kill sperm.
_____ are inserted into uterus to prevent _____ (may also release _____).	_____ from sexual intercourse completely.

 ☑   ☑   ☺ ☑

Topic B5 — Homeostasis and Response

Second Go:
..... /..... /.....

The Menstrual Cycle & Contraception

Stages of the Menstrual Cycle

Stage 1   Stage 2   Stage 3   Stage 4   Next cycle

Stage 1 — _____ . _____ .

Stage 2 — Uterus lining _____
_____ ready to _____ .

Stage 3 — _____
— this is called _____ .

Stage 4 — Wall is maintained. If _____ ,
_____ and _____ .

Four Hormones That Control the Menstrual Cycle

1 FSH (_____) — **3** LH (_____)
_____ . — _____ .

2 Oestrogen _____
_____ . **4** Progesterone _____
_____ .

Contraception

CONTRACEPTION — _____

Hormonal methods	Non-hormonal methods
Oral contraceptive pills	Condoms and
The contraceptive implant	Sterilisation —
Injections or	

Mixed Practice Quizzes

Nice one, you've made it to the end of the topic. Hopefully you'll know enough from p.65-72 to be able to ace these four fabulous practice quizzes.

Quiz 1   Date: ...... / ...... / ......

1) What is sterilisation (in terms of contraception)?
2) Which two structures does the central nervous system consist of?
3) Name a method of contraception that works by inhibiting **FSH**.
4) Give two ways in which the effects of hormones and nerves are different.
5) Do reflexes involve the conscious or unconscious parts of the brain?
6) Which gland is known as the 'master gland'?
7) Describe the cause of Type 2 diabetes.
8) What are the three components of a control system in the body?
9) What hormone is produced in the testes?
10) a) What is ovulation?
    b) Which hormone stimulates ovulation?

Total:

Quiz 2   Date: ...... / ...... / ......

1) Which organ detects changes in blood glucose level?
2) Give two examples of hormonal contraceptive methods and two examples of non-hormonal contraceptive methods.
3) What is the role of a coordination centre in a control system?
4) Give two different types of effector in the body.
5) Why are reflex arcs important?
6) Is obesity a major risk factor for Type 1 diabetes or Type 2 diabetes?
7) a) What is the main reproductive hormone in women?
    b) Where is this hormone produced?
8) What type of neurone connects receptors to the central nervous system?
9) Define 'homeostasis'.
10) Where do eggs mature, in the ovary or in the uterus?

Total:

Mixed Practice Quizzes

Quiz 3   Date: ...... / ...... / ......

1) Which hormone is released when blood glucose level is too high?

2) What are stimuli?

3) What is the role of an effector in a control system?

4) Which method of contraception is effective for longer, the contraceptive implant or the injection?

5) What is the endocrine system?

6) What hormone is produced by the adrenal glands?

7) Why do humans need a nervous system?

8) True or false? In Type 1 diabetes, the pancreas produces too much insulin.

9) Which hormone causes an egg to mature in an ovary?

10) How is pregnancy prevented by: a) diaphragms? b) intrauterine devices?

Total:

Quiz 4   Date: ...... / ...... / ......

1) Which contraceptive method disables or kills sperm?

2) How is homeostasis important for enzyme action?

3) What is a neurone?

4) Give three examples of things in the body that are maintained by automatic control systems.

5) What triggers the development of secondary sexual characteristics during puberty?

6) a) What is a synapse?
   b) How is a nerve signal transferred across a synapse?

7) How do hormones travel around the body to reach target organs?

8) What is the treatment for: a) Type 1 diabetes?   b) Type 2 diabetes?

9) Which type of neurone passes impulses from the CNS to effectors?

10) What is the purpose of contraception?

Total:

DNA

First Go:
..... / ..... / .....

Genetic Material

DeoxyriboNucleic Acid — the chemical a cell's [_____] is made from.

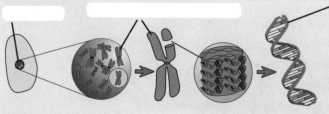

DNA is a [_____]
made up of [_____]
[_____] coiled
into a [_____].

CHROMOSOMES — [_____] of DNA that normally come in [_____].

Humans have [____] pairs. The 23rd pair carries genes which decide a person's [_____].

XY	

XX	

Genes

GENE — a [_____] of
DNA found on a [_____].

Each gene codes for a particular
sequence of [_____],
which are put together to make a
[_____].

20 different [_____]

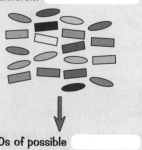

1000s of possible [_____]

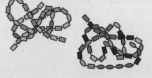

Genomes

GENOME — an organism's entire
set of [_____].

The complete
[_____]
has been worked out.

[_____] linked
to diseases can be
[_____].

Tiny differences in
[_____]
can be studied.

This helps us
better understand
[_____]
so we can develop
effective treatments.

This helps us trace
the migration
patterns of
[_____].

DNA

Genetic Material

D................... N................ A............ —

CHROMOSOMES — _____ .

Humans have _____ . The _____ carries genes which _____ .

X.....			X.....	

Genes

GENE —

Each gene codes for

Genomes

GENOME —

The complete

Genes linked to

can be studied.

This helps us better

This helps us trace

Topic B6 — Inheritance, Variation and Evolution

Reproduction

Asexual and Sexual Reproduction

	Asexual	Sexual
Parents		
Cell division		Meiosis and mitosis
Produces	offspring	Offspring containing a of the parents' genes

Meiosis

Meiosis produces cells with .

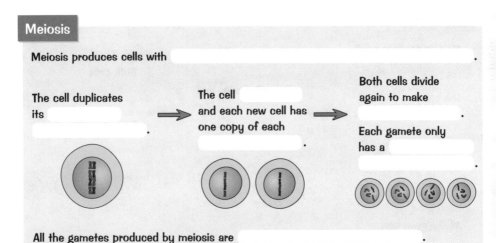

The cell duplicates its .

The cell and each new cell has one copy of each .

Both cells divide again to make .

Each gamete only has a .

All the gametes produced by meiosis are .

Gametes

Gametes are formed by in the .

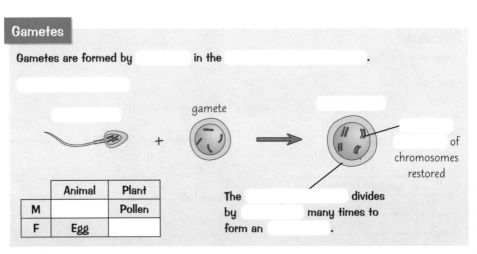

gamete

+ number of chromosomes restored

The divides by many times to form an .

	Animal	Plant
M		Pollen
F	Egg	

Topic B6 — Inheritance, Variation and Evolution

Reproduction

Asexual and Sexual Reproduction

	Asexual	Sexual
Parents		
Cell division		
Produces		

Meiosis

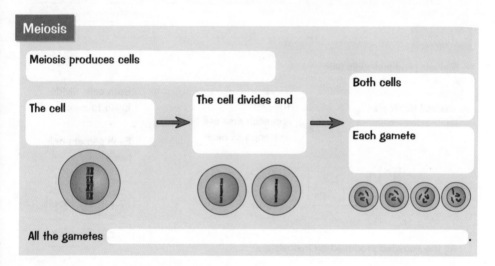

Meiosis produces cells

The cell

The cell divides and

Both cells

Each gamete

All the gametes   .

Gametes

Gametes are formed   .

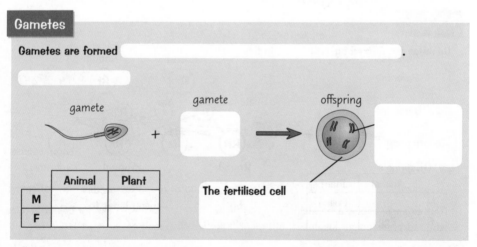

gamete   +   gamete   →   offspring

The fertilised cell

	Animal	Plant
M		
F		

Topic B6 — Inheritance, Variation and Evolution

Genetic Diagrams

Genetic Terms

ALLELE	
DOMINANT	An _____ that is always _____.
RECESSIVE	An _____ that is only expressed when _____.
HOMOZYGOUS	Both of an organism's alleles for a _____ are the _____.
HETEROZYGOUS	An organism's alleles for a _____ are _____.
GENOTYPE	
PHENOTYPE	The _____ an organism has.

Two Types of Genetic Diagrams

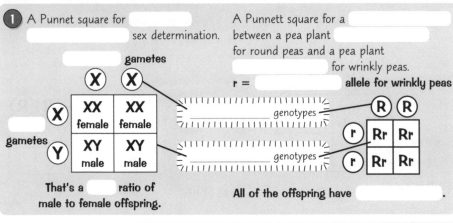

1 A Punnet square for _____ _____ sex determination.

gametes

	X	X
X	XX female	XX female
Y	XY male	XY male

gametes

That's a _____ ratio of male to female offspring.

A Punnett square for a _____ between a pea plant _____ for round peas and a pea plant _____ for wrinkly peas.

r = _____ allele for wrinkly peas

_____ genotypes
_____ genotypes

	R	R
r	Rr	Rr
r	Rr	Rr

All of the offspring have _____.

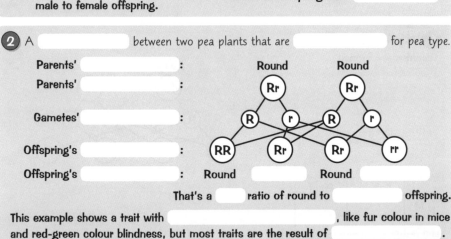

2 A _____ between two pea plants that are _____ for pea type.

Parents' _____ :
Parents' _____ :

Gametes' _____ :

Offspring's _____ :

Offspring's _____ :

Round   Round
(Rr)   (Rr)

(R) (r)   (R) (r)

(RR) (Rr)   (Rr) (rr)

Round _____   Round _____

That's a _____ ratio of round to _____ offspring.

This example shows a trait with _____, like fur colour in mice and red-green colour blindness, but most traits are the result of _____.

Genetic Diagrams

Genetic Terms

ALLELE	
DOMINANT	
RECESSIVE	
	Both of an organism's alleles for a trait are the same.
	An organism's alleles for a trait are different.
GENOTYPE	
PHENOTYPE	

Two Types of Genetic Diagrams

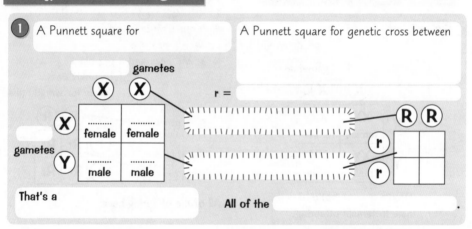

1 A Punnett square for _____

A Punnett square for genetic cross between _____

_____ gametes

(X) (X)

r = _____

gametes (X) | female | female |
(Y) | male | male |

(R)(R)

(r) [grid]
(r)

That's a _____

All of the _____.

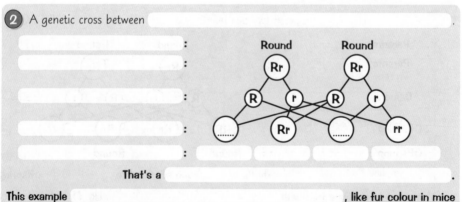

2 A genetic cross between _____

_____ :

_____ :

_____ :

_____ :

_____ :

Round   Round
(Rr)   (Rr)

(R) (r)   (R) (r)

(....) (Rr)   (....) (rr)

That's a _____.

This example _____, like fur colour in mice

and red-green colour blindness, but _____.

Inherited Disorders

Polydactyly

INHERITED DISORDERS —
disorders caused by ⬚
that are inherited from the ⬚.

POLYDACTYLY — a ⬚
where a baby's born with extra
⬚. It's caused
by a ⬚.

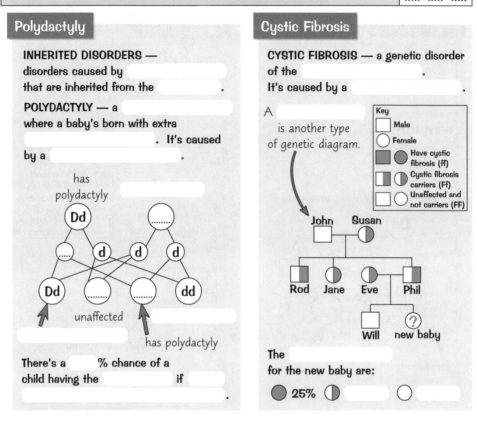

has
polydactyly ⬚

There's a ⬚ % chance of a
child having the ⬚ if
⬚.

Cystic Fibrosis

CYSTIC FIBROSIS — a genetic disorder
of the ⬚.
It's caused by a ⬚.

A ⬚
is another type
of genetic diagram.

Key
- ☐ Male
- ◯ Female
- ⬛◗ Have cystic fibrosis (ff)
- ◨◖ Cystic fibrosis carriers (Ff)
- ☐◯ Unaffected and not carriers (FF)

The ⬚
for the new baby are:
- ◗ 25%   ◖ ⬚   ◯ ⬚

Embryonic Screening

Against Embryonic Screening	For Embryonic Screening
Screening is ⬚.	It will help to stop ⬚.
People might want to screen their embryos so they can pick the ⬚.	Treating disorders costs the ⬚.
It implies that people with genetic problems are '⬚'.	There are ⬚ to stop it going ⬚.

Topic B6 — Inheritance, Variation and Evolution

Inherited Disorders

Polydactyly

INHERITED DISORDERS —

POLYDACTYLY —

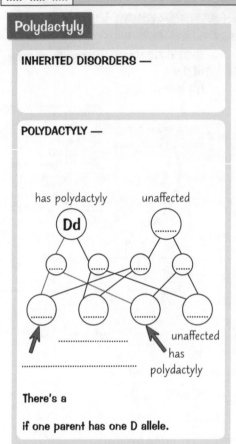

has polydactyly   unaffected

Dd

....

....

....

....

unaffected

....

has
polydactyly

There's a

if one parent has one D allele.

Cystic Fibrosis

CYSTIC FIBROSIS —

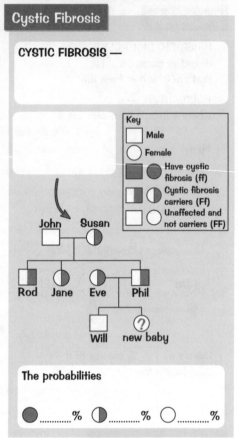

Key
- ☐ Male
- ○ Female
- ◼ ⬤ Have cystic fibrosis (ff)
- ◫ ◑ Cystic fibrosis carriers (Ff)
- ☐ ○ Unaffected and not carriers (FF)

John   Susan

Rod   Jane   Eve   Phil

Will   new baby

The probabilities

⬤ .... %   ◑ .... %   ○ .... %

Embryonic Screening

Against Embryonic Screening	For Embryonic Screening
	It will help
People might want	
It implies that	There are

Topic B6 — Inheritance, Variation and Evolution

Mixed Practice Quizzes

Time for some more quiz questions now, folks. These quizzes are based on p.75-82 so get ready to test your knowledge of DNA, reproduction and genetics.

Quiz 1   Date: ...... / ...... / ......

1) What is polydactyly?
2) What is an allele?
3) Give the names of the gametes produced by plants.
4) How many pairs of chromosomes do human body cells have?
5) Give three arguments against embryonic screening for inherited disorders.
6) In a genetic diagram, does an upper case letter usually represent a dominant or recessive allele?
7) How many parents are needed for asexual reproduction?
8) How many gametes are produced from a single cell undergoing meiosis?
9) What is a gene?
10) How many strands is a DNA molecule made up of?

Total:

Quiz 2   Date: ...... / ...... / ......

1) What are inherited disorders caused by?
2) Is the allele that causes cystic fibrosis recessive or dominant?
3) Which type of reproduction involves meiosis: asexual or sexual?
4) How many pairs of a person's chromosomes determine their sex?
5) What do the letters written above and alongside a Punnett square represent?
6) Give an example of a characteristic that is controlled by a single gene.
7) How is the number of chromosomes in a gamete different to the number of chromosomes in a fertilised egg?
8) What is a genome?
9) Describe the shape of a DNA molecule.
10) What happens to a cell's genetic information before it starts to divide by meiosis?

Total:

Topic B6 — Inheritance, Variation and Evolution

Mixed Practice Quizzes

Date: ...... / ...... / ......

1) What does homozygous mean?
2) True or false? A dominant allele is always expressed.
3) Which sex chromosomes does a female have: XY or XX?
4) Give two benefits of scientists understanding the complete human genome.
5) What kind of cell division does a fertilised cell undergo to grow into an embryo?
6) What is cystic fibrosis?
7) What is an organism's phenotype?
8) Give three arguments for embryonic screening for inherited disorders.
9) Are most characteristics caused by a single gene or multiple genes interacting?
10) True or false? Meiosis produces genetically identical cells.

Total:

Quiz 4 Date: ...... / ...... / ......

1) What are chromosomes?
2) If an organism has two different alleles for a trait, is the organism heterozygous or homozygous for that trait?
3) True or false? Polydactyly is caused by a dominant allele.
4) What is an organism's genotype?
5) Name the chemical that a cell's nuclear genetic material is made from.
6) How many copies of a recessive allele need to be present for it to be expressed?
7) Name the process in which the chromosomes from a male and female gamete get combined.
8) What does a gene code for?
9) True or false? Gametes are formed by mitosis in the reproductive organs.
10) Which type of reproduction produces offspring that are genetically identical?

Total:

Variation and Evolution

Variation

VARIATION — differences in the .... of organisms.

Genetic variation
Differences in the .... individuals inherit
cause variation ....
This variation is usually ....

E.g. eye colour

.... cause these differences in genes. Mutations occur ....

	Most mutations	Some mutations	Very few mutations
Effect on phenotype		Slight	New

Environmental variation
Differences in the ....
in which an organism develops
....

E.g. leaf colour

Genetic and environmental variation
For most characteristics, ...
is caused by both .... and
the ....

E.g. plant height

Natural Selection

Charles .... came up with the theory of evolution
by natural selection: all of ....
have evolved from .... that first
started to develop over .... years ago.

The theory is now ....
.... as scientists have
found that characteristics are
....
....

Species show
....
....

Organisms with the ⟶

These organisms are
....

⬇

Limited resources
mean organisms are in
....

....
....
for the environment are
more likely to survive.

The beneficial characteristics
are passed on and
gradually become ....
.... in the population.

Two populations of a species can evolve in ....
If they change so much that they can no longer .... with one another to
produce .... , then they have become separate ....

 ☑   ☑   ☑

Variation and Evolution

Variation

VARIATION — differences ....

Genetic variation

Differences in the

This variation is

Mutations cause

Mutations

E.g. _____

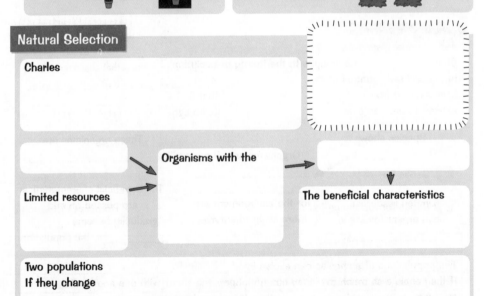

	Most mutations	Some mutations	Very few mutations
Effect on phenotype			

Environmental variation

Differences in the

E.g. _____

Genetic and environmental variation

For most characteristics,

E.g. _____

Natural Selection

Charles

Organisms with the

Limited resources

The beneficial characteristics

Two populations
If they change

Uses of Genetics

Selective Breeding

SELECTIVE BREEDING — breeding plants or animals for [_____].
Four uses of selective breeding:

1 Greater [_____] production.

3 A good, gentle [_____] in dogs.

2 Big or unusual [_____].

4 [_____] in crops.

Individuals with [_____]
[_____]
bred together. —

Repeated over [_____].

Humans have used selective breeding for
....
However, it can lead to
....

Genetic Engineering

Genetic engineering transfers a [_____] responsible for a [_____]
from one organism's genome into another organism.

The process involves [_____] out of one organism and putting it into
[_____] cells.

Three uses of genetic engineering:

1 Genes for producing [_____] transferred to bacteria.

2 Genes for [_____] fruit transferred to crops.

3 Genes for resistance to [_____] transferred to crops.

Pros of GM crops	Cons of GM crops
	Could reduce
Helps people with diets that lack nutrients	Concerns about
Already being grown	may spread into the wild

Uses of Genetics

Selective Breeding

SELECTIVE BREEDING —

Four uses of selective breeding:

1️⃣

3️⃣

2️⃣

4️⃣

Individuals with

Humans have used
_____
_____
_____.
However, _____
_____.

Genetic Engineering

Genetic engineering transfers

The process involves

Three uses of genetic engineering:

1️⃣

2️⃣

3️⃣

Pros of GM crops:	Cons of GM crops:

Topic B6 — Inheritance, Variation and Evolution

Fossils and Antibiotic Resistance

Fossils

FOSSILS — remains of organisms from

_____ .

Three ways that fossils form:

1 Gradual replacement by _____ —
happens to _____ .

2 _____ — e.g. footprints, burrows and rootlet traces.

3 Preservation — in places where conditions _____ ,
parts of organisms can be _____ .

Fossils show _____ organisms have
changed as _____ but there's uncertainty over
how life began because the _____ :

Many early forms of life were _____ and _____

Some fossils have been destroyed
by _____ .

Studying fossils and
antibiotic-resistant bacteria
contributed to the

_____

being widely accepted.

Antibiotic-Resistant Bacteria

Bacteria can _____ because
they _____ .

_____ is a type of
antibiotic-resistant bacterium.

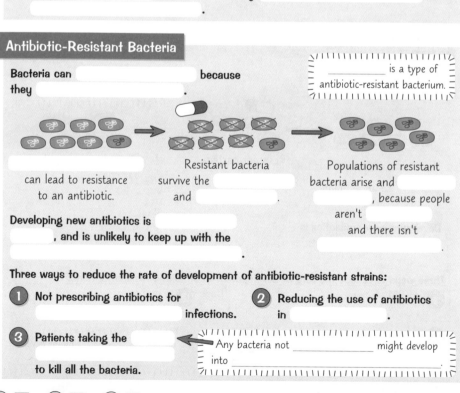

_____
can lead to resistance
to an antibiotic.

Resistant bacteria
survive the _____
and _____ .

Populations of resistant
bacteria arise and _____ , because people
aren't _____
and there isn't _____

Developing new antibiotics is _____
, and is unlikely to keep up with the

_____

Three ways to reduce the rate of development of antibiotic-resistant strains:

1 Not prescribing antibiotics for
_____ infections.

2 Reducing the use of antibiotics
in _____ .

3 Patients taking the _____
to kill all the bacteria.

Any bacteria not _____ might develop
into _____ .

 ✓ ✓ ✓

Topic B6 — Inheritance, Variation and Evolution

Fossils and Antibiotic Resistance

Fossils

FOSSILS —

Three ways that fossils form:

1

2

3 Preservation —

> Studying fossils and
> antibiotic-resistant bacteria
> ....
> ....
> ....

Fossils show how

is incomplete:

Many early forms of life were

Some fossils have been

Antibiotic-Resistant Bacteria

Bacteria can

> .... is a type of
> ....

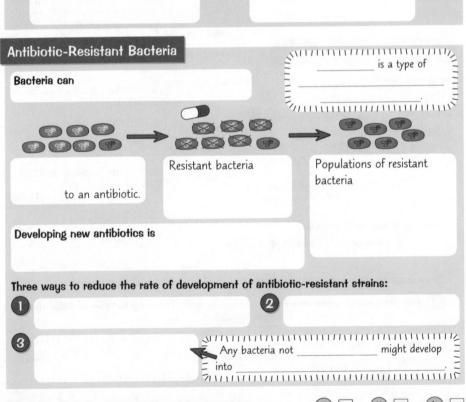

to an antibiotic.

Resistant bacteria

Populations of resistant
bacteria

Developing new antibiotics is

Three ways to reduce the rate of development of antibiotic-resistant strains:

1

2

3

> Any bacteria not .... might develop
> into ....

Classification and Extinction

The Linnaean System

The Linnaean system was developed by [_____].

It organises organisms by their [_____] [_____] into these groups.

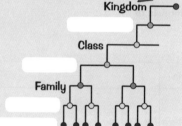

Kingdom

[_____]

Class

[_____]

Family

[_____]

[_____]

[_____] system

Genus [_____]

E.g. *Homo* *sapiens*

Developments in Classification

[_____] showed us more about [_____] of organisms.

Improved chemical analysis increased our understanding of [_____].

New models of [_____] proposed, e.g. Carl Woese's [_____].

Bacteria	
Archaea	a different type of [_____] usually found in extreme places
Eukaryota	including protists, [_____]

Evolutionary Trees

Evolutionary trees show how scientists think [_____] are [_____].

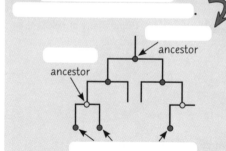

[_____]

[_____] ancestor

ancestor

[_____]

Data source	Living species	Extinct species
	Current [_____] data	Fossil data

Extinction

EXTINCTION — when [_____] of a [_____].

[_____] change

New [_____]

New [_____]

[_____]

[_____] events

Classification and Extinction

The Linnaean System

The Linnaean system

It organises organisms

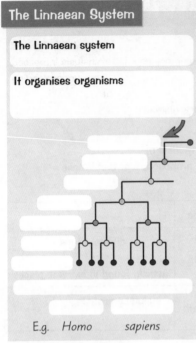

E.g.   *Homo   sapiens*

Developments in Classification

Better microscopes showed us more about

Improved chemical analysis

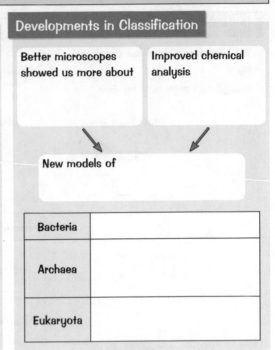

New models of

Bacteria	
Archaea	
Eukaryota	

Evolutionary Trees

Evolutionary trees

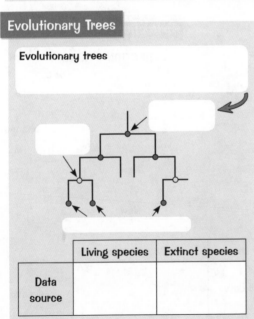

	Living species	Extinct species
Data source		

Extinction

EXTINCTION —

Topic B6 — Inheritance, Variation and Evolution

Mixed Practice Quizzes

Have a go at the following quizzes to see if you could be classified as a biology genius. All the questions are based on what you can remember from p.85-92.

Quiz 1   Date: ...... / ...... / ......

1) What are fossils?
2) How can genetic engineering benefit fruit production?
3) How have better microscopes led to developments in classification?
4) What is the theory of evolution by natural selection?
5) Give a useful substance that genetically engineered bacterial cells can be used to produce.
6) Give two reasons why the fossil record is incomplete.
7) Give one problem that can be caused by selective breeding.
8) Who proposed the three domain system of classification?
9) Give three ways to reduce the rate of development of antibiotic-resistant strains of bacteria.
10) What is the difference between genetic and environmental variation?

Total:

Quiz 2   Date: ...... / ...... / ......

1) What is extinction?
2) What is variation?
3) Give four groups of organisms within Eukaryota.
4) What do evolutionary trees show?
5) Give two risks of GM crops.
6) True or false? Fossils and antibiotic-resistant bacteria are used as evidence for the theory of evolution by natural selection.
7) What is used to organise organisms in the Linnaean system?
8) Why are bacteria able to evolve quickly?
9) Give four characteristics that selective breeding can be used to improve.
10) True or false? Genetic variation within a species is usually extensive.

Total:

Topic B6 — Inheritance, Variation and Evolution

Mixed Practice Quizzes

Quiz 3 Date: ...... / ...... / ......

1) What is selective breeding?
2) Give two pros of GM crops.
3) Name an antibiotic-resistant strain of bacteria.
4) How long ago did the simple life forms that all living species evolved from first start to develop?
5) Looking at the fossil record, why is it difficult to be certain how life began?
6) In the binomial name of a species what comes first: genus or species?
7) What causes environmental variation within a population?
8) Give the seven levels of classification used in the Linnaean system.
9) Give five factors that can cause extinction.
10) Give two reasons why antibiotic-resistant bacteria are able to spread so easily.

Total:

Quiz 4 Date: ...... / ...... / ......

1) Who developed the Linnaean system?
2) What is genetic engineering?
3) What type of organisms are Archaea?
4) True or false? Mutations often result in a new phenotype.
5) How does antibiotic resistance arise in a population of bacteria?
6) How have improvements in chemical analysis led to developments in classification?
7) Give three ways that fossils can form.
8) Describe the process of selective breeding.
9) Give two types of data used to produce evolutionary trees.
10) When would two evolving populations of a species be considered to have become separate species?

Total:

Basics of Ecology

Definitions of Ecological Terms

	All the organisms of one species living in a habitat.
COMMUNITY	
STABLE COMMUNITY	A community in which all species and environmental factors are in ....
ECOSYSTEM	The interaction of a community of ....
	A feature that enables an organism to survive in the conditions of its normal habitat.
	Each species in a community depending upon other species for things, e.g. ...., food, shelter or seed dispersal.

Due to ...., change in
an ecosystem (e.g. ....
.........................) can affect the whole community.

Factors Affecting Communities

Both .... (living) and .... (non-living) factors can affect organisms in a community:

Light intensity

Wind and ....

.... level

Organisms compete for:
light, ...,
minerals, ...,
food, ...,

.... (for plants)

Competition

New ....

Food availability
.... (for aquatic animals)

Temperature

New pathogens

Soil .... and ....

One species may
.... another so that
numbers are ....

Three Types of Adaptation

1 Structural   2 ....   3 ....

.... — organisms that are adapted to live in extreme conditions,
such as ...., high pressure or high salt concentration
(e.g. ....).

Second Go:
...... /...... /......

Basics of Ecology

Definitions of Ecological Terms

POPULATION:
COMMUNITY:
STABLE COMMUNITY: A community in which
ECOSYSTEM:
ADAPTATION:
INTERDEPENDENCE:

Due to _____, change in an ecosystem _____

Factors Affecting Communities

_____ factors can affect organisms in a community:

intensity

Organisms compete for:

Competition

Temperature

O_2 level

One species may _____

Three Types of Adaptation

1.
2.
3.

EXTREMOPHILES —

Food Chains and Biodiversity

Food Chains

[   ]   **CONSUMER**   [   ]   **CONSUMER**

— a plant or [   ]   — an animal that eats   — an animal that eats
that makes glucose by   [   ] and   [   ]
[   ].   may be eaten by   and may be eaten by
All food chains start   [   ]   [   ].
with a [   ].   [   ].

[   ] — a consumer that kills and eats other animals ([   ]).

BIOMASS — [   ].

[   ] stored in biomass is transferred along food chains and used by
other organisms to [   ].

Predator-Prey Cycles

In a [   ] the
numbers of predators and prey rise and
fall in cycles:

Prey population
increases

Predator
population
[   ]

[   ]

Prey
population
decreases

Predator-prey cycles are always out of
phase with each other, as it

[   ]

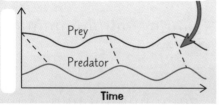

Prey

Predator

Time

Biodiversity

BIODIVERSITY —

[   ]

[   ]

(lots of different species)

[   ]

of one species on another for
things like [   ].
and the maintenance of the

[   ].

[   ]

For [   ]

[   ], it's important that a
good level of biodiversity is maintained.

Sadly, _____
_____ — we've only
recently started taking measures to stop this.

Topic B7 — Ecology

Food Chains and Biodiversity

Food Chains

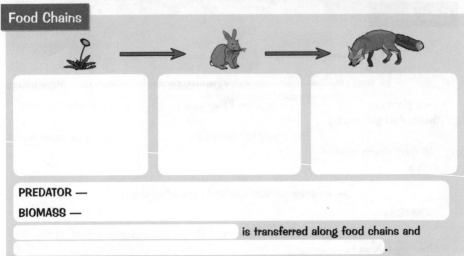

PREDATOR —

BIOMASS —

_____ is transferred along food chains and

_____ .

Predator-Prey Cycles

In a _____ the numbers of predators and prey rise and fall in cycles:

Prey population increases

Predator-prey cycles are always

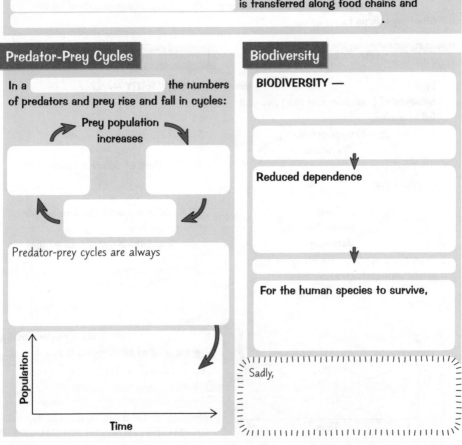

Population

Time

Biodiversity

BIODIVERSITY —

Reduced dependence

For the human species to survive,

Sadly,

Cycling of Materials

Recycling Materials

Materials are cycled through the [____] and [____] parts of an ecosystem.

[_____], absorption from [____]

Materials in the ⟶ Materials in

[____]

⟵ [____], death and decay

Materials decay because they're broken down by [_____].
Decay puts materials like [_____] back into the soil.

The Water Cycle

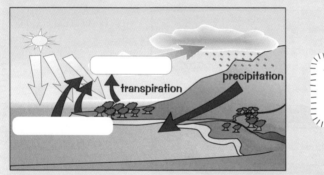

[____]

transpiration

precipitation

[____]

[____] provides fresh water for plants and animals on land.

The Carbon Cycle

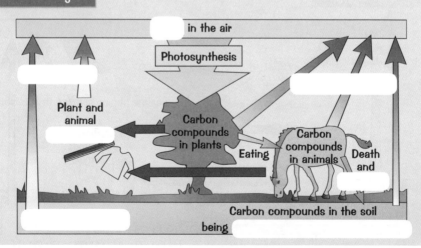

[____] in the air

Photosynthesis

[____]

Plant and animal

Carbon compounds in plants

Carbon compounds in animals

Eating

Death and [____]

[____]

Carbon compounds in the soil

being [____]

Topic B7 — Ecology

Cycling of Materials

Recycling Materials

Materials are cycled through the _____.

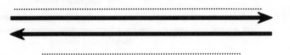

Materials decay because
Decay puts

The Water Cycle

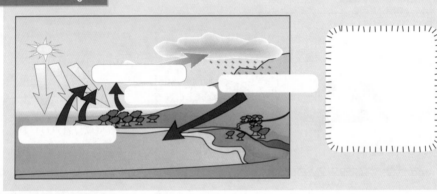

The Carbon Cycle

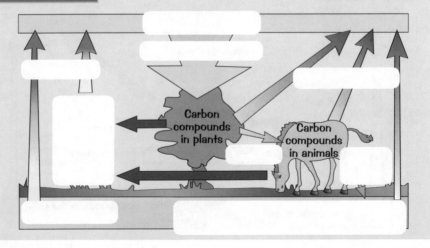

Carbon compounds in plants

Carbon compounds in animals

 ✓ ✓ ✓

Human Effects on Ecosystems

Global Warming

The Earth is gradually heating up as a result of

trapped

Three consequences of global warming could be:

greenhouse gases
(e.g.
and)

1 Rising sea levels (so).

2 A change in the of some organisms.

3 A decrease in (as some species may become extinct).

Land Use and Deforestation

Humans use land for things like , , and
. This means there's
.

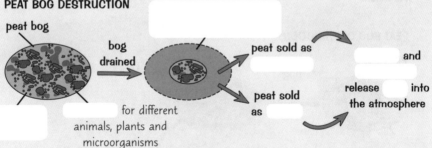

PEAT BOG DESTRUCTION

peat bog

bog
drained

peat sold as

and

peat sold
as

release into
the atmosphere

for different
animals, plants and
microorganisms

— the cutting down of forests.

It has been done on a large-scale in areas in order to:

* clear land for and ,

* grow crops to make .

Second Go:
..... / ..... / .....

Human Effects on Ecosystems

Global Warming

The Earth is _____
as a result of _____
_____
_____ .

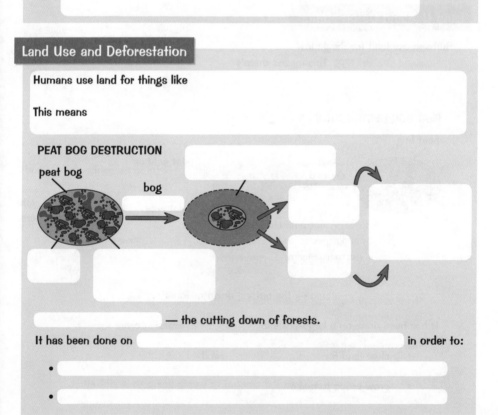

Three consequences of global warming could be:

1 _____

2 _____

3 _____

Land Use and Deforestation

Humans use land for things like _____

This means _____

PEAT BOG DESTRUCTION

peat bog _____

bog _____

_____ — the cutting down of forests.

It has been done on _____ in order to:

• _____

• _____

Maintaining Ecosystems

Pollution

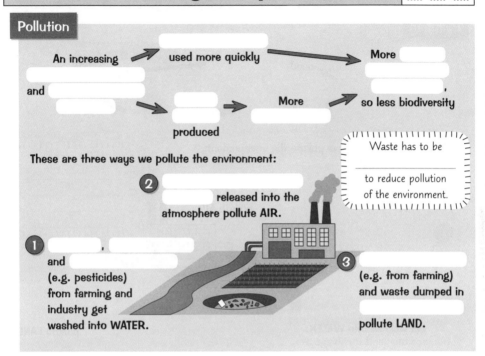

An increasing ⬚ → used more quickly ⬚ → More ⬚
⬚ ⬚

and ⬚ ⬚ → ⬚ → More ⬚ ⬚ so less biodiversity
⬚ produced

These are three ways we pollute the environment:

Waste has to be .... to reduce pollution of the environment.

2 ⬚
⬚ released into the atmosphere pollute AIR.

1 ⬚, ⬚
and ⬚
(e.g. pesticides)
from farming and
industry get
washed into WATER.

3 ⬚
(e.g. from farming)
and waste dumped in
⬚
pollute LAND.

Five Programmes to Protect Ecosystems

1 ⬚ programmes —
⬚ species are ⬚
⬚ to make sure the species survive.

Programmes like these are set up to reduce the ....

2 Habitat restoration — rare habitats like
⬚, ⬚ and ⬚
⬚ are protected and regenerated.

3 ⬚ —
these are reintroduced around fields where only a single crop type
is grown, creating ⬚.

4 Government regulations — e.g. ⬚
⬚.

5 ⬚ — reduces the amount of waste going to landfill sites.

 ✓   ✓   ✓

Maintaining Ecosystems

Pollution

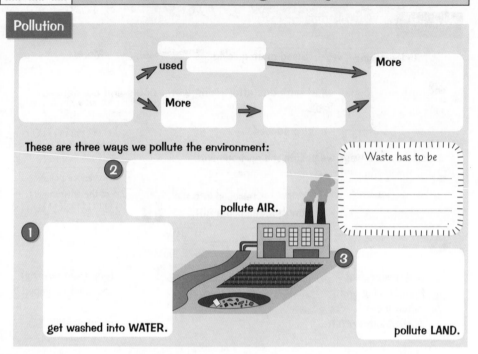

used _____ ⟶ More _____

More ⟶ _____ ⟶ _____

These are three ways we pollute the environment:

2 _____ pollute AIR.

Waste has to be
_____
_____
_____

1 _____ get washed into WATER.

3 _____ pollute LAND.

Five Programmes to Protect Ecosystems

1 Breeding programmes —

Programmes like these are
set up _____
_____
_____

2 _____ — _____
_____ are protected and regenerated.

3 Hedgerows and field margins —

4 _____ — e.g. to reduce deforestation
and _____ .

5 _____ — reduces the amount of _____
_____ .

 ☑ ☺ ☑ ☺ ☑

Mixed Practice Quizzes

Predator-prey, water, carbon — there have been so many cycles on pages 95-104 that you might be feeling dizzy, but it's not over yet... Onwards to the quizzes.

Quiz 1   Date: ...... / ...... / ......

1) In the water cycle, what happens after rising water cools and condenses?

2) Give four examples of things that species in a community might depend upon other species for.

3) Describe two ways that toxic chemicals pollute the natural environment.

4) Give three things that animals compete for.

5) Give two reasons why deforestation is happening in tropical areas.

6) How is carbon taken out of the air in the carbon cycle?

7) What are secondary consumers?

8) What are the three types of adaptation organisms may have?

9) Give two ways that government regulations could protect ecosystems.

10) How does burning fossil fuels affect the CO_2 concentration of the air?

Total:

Quiz 2   Date: ...... / ...... / ......

1) What is the difference between a population and a community?

2) How does high biodiversity lead to stable ecosystems?

3) How does the use of peat for fuel have an environmental impact?

4) Explain two ways in which global warming could affect organisms.

5) Give a material that microorganisms involved in decay return to the soil.

6) How do breeding programmes help to protect biodiversity?

7) Describe what might happen to the population of a species when it is outcompeted by another species.

8) Give four biotic factors that can affect organisms in a community.

9) Give one reason why maintaining a good level of biodiversity is important.

10) Why are predator-prey cycles always out of phase with each other?

Total:

Mixed Practice Quizzes

Date: ...... / ...... / ......

1) How has the increase in the standard of living resulted in more pollution? ✓
2) Give an example of an extremophile. ✓
3) Give two things that peat is sold for. ✓
4) Give seven abiotic factors that can affect organisms in a community. ✓
5) Programmes that protect and regenerate rare habitats are an example of programmes set up to maintain what? ✓
6) How are carbon compounds in plants transferred to other parts of the carbon cycle? ✓
7) Which stage of the water cycle provides fresh water for organisms on land? ✓
8) What process is carried out by all producers, but not consumers? ✓
9) What is a tertiary consumer? ✓
10) Define 'ecosystem'. ✓

Total:

Quiz 4 Date: ...... / ...... / ......

1) Increasing atmospheric levels of what are causing the Earth to warm up? ✓
2) Why have farmers reintroduced hedgerows and field margins in some areas? ✓
3) List four activities that humans commonly use land for. ✓
4) Give two types of organisms that can be producers. ✓
5) Give three ways that water is polluted. ✓
6) What is the definition of a 'stable community'? ✓
7) List four things that plants compete for. ✓
8) Define 'biodiversity'. ✓
9) Give two abiotic factors regarding the soil that may affect organisms in a community. ✓
10) What term describes organisms that are adapted to live in extreme conditions? ✓

Total:

Atomic Structure & Nuclear Symbols

Atomic Structure

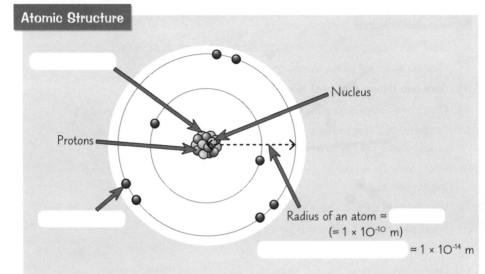

Nucleus

Protons

Radius of an atom ≈ [_____]
(= 1×10^{-10} m)

[_____] ≈ 1×10^{-14} m

Particle	Relative mass	Relative charge
Proton		+1
Neutron	1	
	Very small	−1

Atoms have no overall charge
(number of _____ =
number of _____).

Nuclear Symbols

NUCLEAR SYMBOL — used to describe atoms:

[_____] = total number of protons and neutrons in an atom

$$^{23}_{11}\text{Na}$$

[_____]

Atomic number = number of [_____] in an atom

| Second Go: ..... / ..... / ..... | **Atomic Structure & Nuclear Symbols** |

Atomic Structure

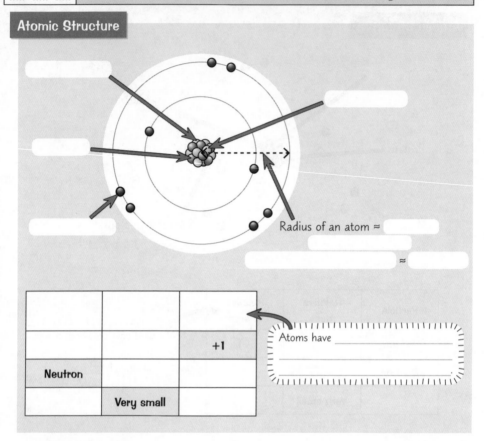

Radius of an atom ≈ _____

_____ ≈ _____

		+1
Neutron		
	Very small	

Atoms have _____

Nuclear Symbols

NUCLEAR SYMBOL — used to _____ :

_____ = → $^{23}_{11}$**Na** ← _____

_____ = _____

Elements and Compounds

Elements

ELEMENTS — substances made up of atoms with the same [_____].

There are about [_____] different elements.

[_____] of an element — atoms with [_____] number of protons but [_____] numbers of neutrons.

[..] (A_r) — the average mass number for an element:

$$A_r = \frac{\text{sum of } (.. \times \text{ isotope mass number})}{\text{total abundance of all isotopes}}$$

Compounds

COMPOUND — substance formed from [_____] elements [_____] in fixed proportions.

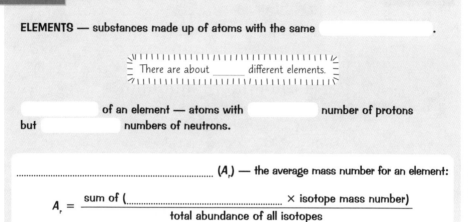

compound

elements

molecules

MOLECULE — particle containing two or more non-metal atoms bonded [_____].

Molecules can be [_____] (if they only have [_____] of atom) or compounds.

At least one new substance is made in a chemical reaction. You can usually [_____].

     Topic C1 — Atomic Structure and the Periodic Table

Second Go:
...../...../.....

Elements and Compounds

Elements

ELEMENTS —

There are about .... different elements.

.... (A_r) —

the average .... :

A_r =

Compounds

COMPOUND —

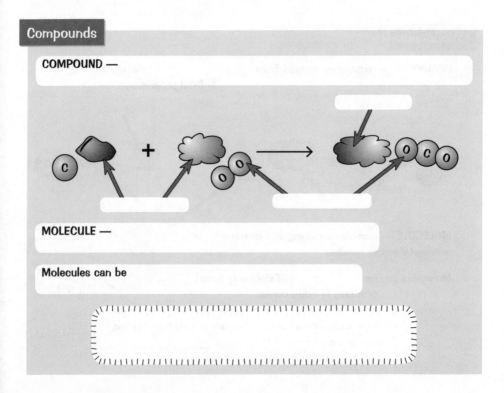

MOLECULE —

Molecules can be

Topic C1 — Atomic Structure and the Periodic Table

Equations, Mixtures & Chromatography

Chemical Formulas and Equations

Chemical formula — shows the _____ in a compound.

E.g. CO_2 ← _____ for every carbon atom

Chemical equation — shows the _____ in a reaction.

_____   **Products**

_____ methane + oxygen → _____ + water

Symbol equation: _____ + $2O_2$ → CO_2 + _____

There must be _____ of each atom on each side so the equation is _____.

The _____ in front of the _____ tell you how many units of that _____ there are.

Mixtures

MIXTURES — substances made up of different _____ or compounds that _____ to each other.

E.g. air is a mixture.

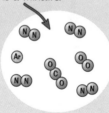

The _____ of a substance aren't affected by being _____.

Mixtures can be separated by .... — these don't involve .... or form ....

Paper Chromatography

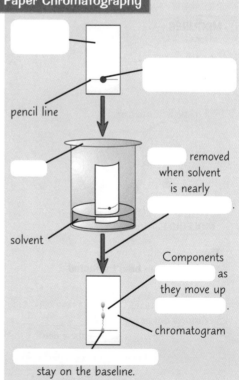

pencil line

_____

solvent

_____ removed when solvent is nearly _____.

Components _____ as they move up _____.

chromatogram

_____ stay on the baseline.

 ✓ ✓ ✓

Topic C1 — Atomic Structure and the Periodic Table

Equations, Mixtures & Chromatography

Chemical Formulas and Equations

Chemical formula —

E.g. CO_2

Chemical equation —

methane + → + water

+ $2O_2$ → CO_2 +

There must be the

Mixtures

MIXTURES —

E.g. air is a mixture.

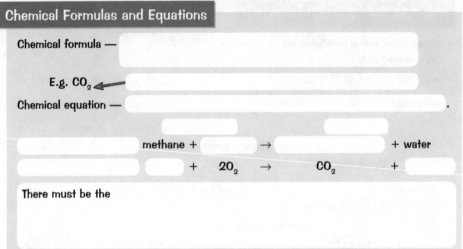

The

aren't affected

.

Mixtures can be
_____ — these don't
_____
_____.

Paper Chromatography

More Separation Techniques

Filtration

FILTRATION — separates [____] from liquids and [____].

It can be used to separate out [____], or [____] by removing [____].

Solid left in the [____]

Evaporation

EVAPORATION — separates [____] from solution.

evaporating dish

and dry out as solvent [____].

Slowly [____] solution.

Evaporation is [____], but can't be used if the [____] when heated.

Crystallisation

CRYSTALLISATION — also separates [____] from solution.

Heat solution, but [____] when [____] start to form.

[____] form as solution cools.

Filter out [____] and leave to [____].

Use crystallisation for salts that [____], or if you want [____].

Two Types of Distillation

1 Simple distillation

[____]

The part with the [____] evaporates first.

water out

[____] and condenses.

[____] can't separate liquids with [____], but fractional distillation can.

water in

heat

[____]

2 Fractional distillation

thermometer

[____]

Liquids reach the [____] when the temperature at the top [____].

fractions collected

fractionating column filled with [____]

mixture of liquids

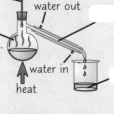

Second Go:
..... /..... /.....

More Separation Techniques

Filtration

FILTRATION —

It can be used

Evaporation

EVAPORATION —

solution.

Evaporation is ...., but can't be used if the ....

Crystallisation

CRYSTALLISATION —

Use crystallisation for ....
....
or if you ....

Two Types of Distillation

1 Simple distillation

The part with the

water in

2 Fractional distillation

115

Atomic and Electronic Structure

First Go:
..... /..... /.....

The History of the Atom

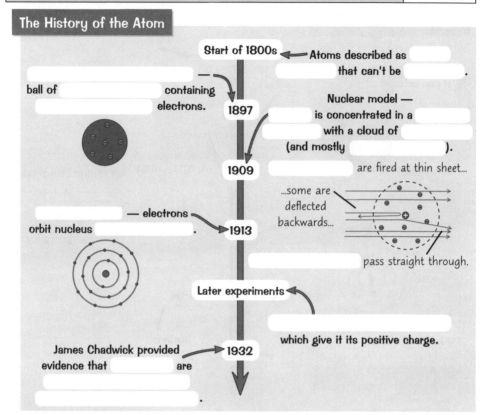

Start of 1800s ← Atoms described as _____ that can't be _____.

ball of _____ containing _____ electrons.

1897

Nuclear model — _____ is concentrated in a _____ with a cloud of _____ (and mostly _____).

1909 _____ are fired at thin sheet...

...some are deflected backwards...

_____ pass straight through.

_____ — electrons orbit nucleus _____.

1913

Later experiments

_____ which give it its positive charge.

James Chadwick provided evidence that _____ are

1932

_____.

Electronic Structure

Electrons occupy _____ — sometimes called energy _____.

Electrons _____ before occupying a new one, starting with the _____.

Lowest energy shells are _____

Shell	.... allowed in shell
1	2
2	
	8

Electronic structure can also be represented as _____ — this one is _____.

 ✓   ✓   ✓ Topic C1 — Atomic Structure and the Periodic Table

Atomic and Electronic Structure

The History of the Atom

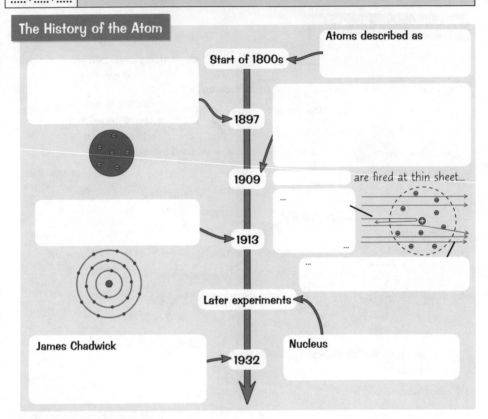

Atoms described as

Start of 1800s

1897

1909

are fired at thin sheet...

...

...

1913

...

Later experiments

Nucleus

James Chadwick

1932

Electronic Structure

Electrons occupy

Electrons

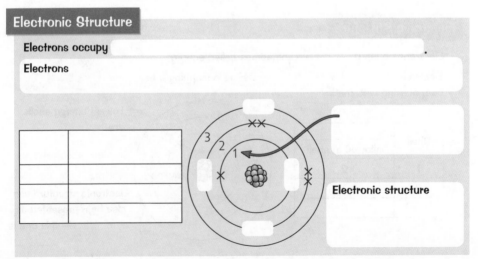

Electronic structure

Topic C1 — Atomic Structure and the Periodic Table ☑ ☑ ☑

Mixed Practice Quizzes

You've made it through the first half of Topic C1. Now have a go at these four quizzes based on p.107-116 and remember to mark yourself when you're done.

Quiz 1   Date: ...... / ...... / ......

1) What is the approximate radius of a nucleus?
2) What is the overall charge of an atom?
3) What type of mixture is simple distillation used to separate?
4) Which part of an atom's nuclear symbol shows the number of protons in an atom of that element?
5) True or false? Mixtures can only be separated by chemical reactions.
6) What does the chemical formula of a compound show?
7) What type of mixture can crystallisation be used to separate?
8) Which scientist provided evidence that neutrons are part of the nucleus?
9) True or false? There are about 100 different elements.
10) How many electrons are allowed in the lowest energy shell of an atom?

Total:

Quiz 2   Date: ...... / ...... / ......

1) True or false? The nucleus of an atom is negatively charged.
2) What happens to the majority of α-particles when they're fired at a thin sheet of atoms?
3) How is the relative atomic mass (A_r) of an element calculated?
4) Define the term 'mixture'.
5) What is the approximate radius of an atom?
6) What is the final step when crystallising a salt?
7) True or false? Each of the particles that make up an atom have the same relative mass.
8) Which part of a mixture of liquids will evaporate first in simple distillation?
9) Where are the electron shells with the lowest energy in an atom?
10) What does the mass number tell you about an atom?

Total:

Topic C1 — Atomic Structure and the Periodic Table

Mixed Practice Quizzes

Quiz 3   Date: ...... / ...... / ......

1) Where does the nuclear model say the mass of an atom is concentrated? ☑
2) What is the relative charge of an electron? ☑
3) Define what is meant by the term 'compound'. ☑
4) What is shown by the large numbers in front of chemical formulas in chemical equations? ☑
5) When should the filter paper be removed from the solvent when carrying out paper chromatography? ☑
6) What is the relative mass of a neutron? ☑
7) Which technique could you use to separate an insoluble solid from a solution? ☑
8) Describe the 'plum pudding' model of the atom. ☑
9) True or false? Atomic number is equal to the number of neutrons in that atom. ☑
10) What did the Bohr model suggest about the structure of the atom? ☑

Total: ☐

Quiz 4   Date: ...... / ...... / ......

1) What name is given to the positively charged particles in an atom? ☑
2) How many electrons are allowed in the second electron shell of an atom? ☑
3) What is the mass of an electron relative to the mass of a proton? ☑
4) What is meant by the term 'isotope'? ☑
5) True or false? Molecules are particles containing a metal atom and a non-metal atom. ☑
6) Give two ways of showing the overall change in a chemical reaction. ☑
7) How many oxygen atoms are present in one molecule of CO_2? ☑
8) What happens to the insoluble components of a mixture being separated by chromatography? ☑
9) Which type of distillation can be used to separate compounds with similar boiling points? ☑
10) Which atomic model shows electrons orbiting the nucleus in fixed shells? ☑

Total: ☐

Topic C1 — Atomic Structure and the Periodic Table

The Periodic Table

Mendeleev's Table

Before atomic structure was discovered, _____
was used to order _____ .

In Mendeleev's Table of Elements, the elements were _____
using _____ , instead of strictly following _____ .

Mendeleev had to _____
in the table to _____ _____ which fitted into
_____ the gaps were _____ .

```
H
Li  Be                                              B   C   N   O   F
Na  Mg                                              Al  Si  P   S   Cl
K   Ca  *   Ti  V   Cr  Mn  Fe  Co  Ni  Cu  Zn  *   *   As  Se  Br
Rb  Sr  Y   Zr  Nb  Mo  *   Ru  Rh  Pd  Ag  Cd  In  Sn  Sb  Te  I
Cs  Ba  *   *   Ta  W   *   Os  Ir  Pt  Au  Hg  Tl  Pb  Bi
```

Mendeleev _____   Discovery of _____ explained
_____ in places where ordering by   why _____ cannot be strictly
_____ didn't fit the pattern.   ordered by _____ .

The Modern Periodic Table

The _____ are ordered by
_____ .

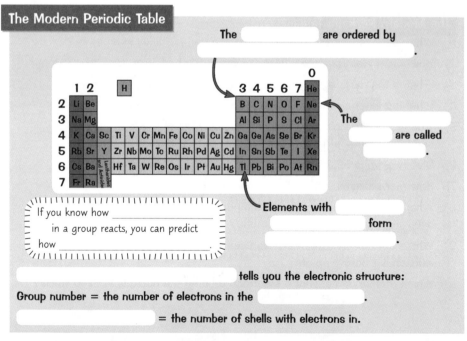

The _____ are called _____ .

Elements with _____
_____ form
_____ .

If you know how _____
in a group reacts, you can predict
how _____ .

_____ tells you the electronic structure:

Group number = the number of electrons in the _____ .

_____ = the number of shells with electrons in.

 ☑   ☑   ☑   Topic C1 — Atomic Structure and the Periodic Table

Second Go:
..... /..... /.....

The Periodic Table

Mendeleev's Table

Before

In Mendeleev's

, instead of   .

Mendeleev had to

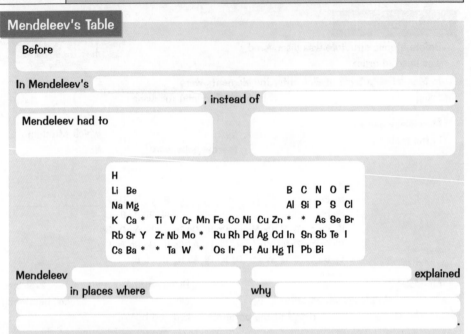

```
H
Li Be                              B  C  N  O  F
Na Mg                             Al Si  P  S  Cl
K  Ca *  Ti  V  Cr Mn Fe Co Ni Cu Zn *  * As Se Br
Rb Sr  Y  Zr Nb Mo *  Ru Rh Pd Ag Cd In Sn Sb Te  I
Cs Ba *  *  Ta  W  *  Os Ir  Pt Au Hg Tl Pb Bi
```

Mendeleev   explained

in places where   why

.

The Modern Periodic Table

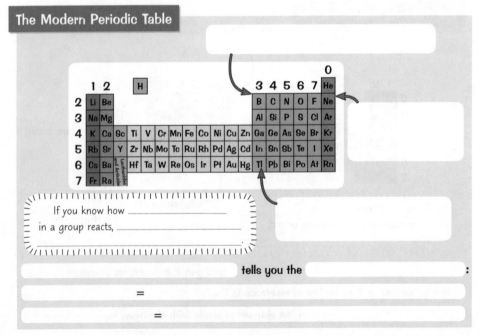

If you know how _____
in a group reacts, _____

tells you the   :

=

=

  ☐ ☐ ☐

Metals and Non-Metals

Reactivity of Metals and Non-Metals

METALS — elements that [_____] when they react.

[_____] — elements that [_____]

[_____]

[_____] .

metals

Atoms tend to react to form [_____] .

	Metals	Non-metals
Get a full outer shell by...		...gaining or sharing electrons
More reactive when they...	...lose electrons more easily	
More reactive towards...	.... of the periodic table	...the top right of the periodic table

Properties of Metals and Non-Metals

These are _____ — they're not true for _____ metal or non-metal.

Appearance		Dull
Strength		Brittle
Melting and boiling points	High	Low
Conductivity	Good .... conductors	.... conductors

Topic C1 — Atomic Structure and the Periodic Table

Metals and Non-Metals

Reactivity of Metals and Non-Metals

METALS —

  — elements that

	Metals	Non-metals
Get a .... by...		
More	...lose electrons more easily	
More	.... of the periodic table	...the top right of the periodic table

Properties of Metals and Non-Metals

Appearance		
Strength		
Melting and boiling points		
Conductivity		

These are _____ — they're
not true for _____ .

Group 1 and Group 0 Elements

Trends in Group 1

[_____] — common name for the [_____].

As you go .... Group 1:		$^{7}_{3}$Li
Reactivity	increases	$^{23}_{11}$Na
Melting and boiling points	....	$^{39}_{19}$K
Relative	increases	$^{85}_{37}$Rb
		$^{133}_{55}$Cs
		$^{223}_{87}$Fr

Properties of Group 1 Metals

Group 1 metals have different properties from most other metals:

They're much [_____].

They're [_____] and softer.

They have [____] melting points.

Reactions of Group 1 Elements

The Group 1 elements only have [_____]

— [_____] to lose it so

they readily form [_____].

They react with a range of substances to form [_____]:

metal + ... → metal hydroxide + hydrogen

metal + chlorine → ....

metal + ... → ....

As reactivity increases ...., the reaction with water becomes more ....

Group 0 Elements

GROUP 0 ELEMENTS — non-metals with [_____].

Their [_____] is stable so they are [_____].

All Group 0 elements are [_____] at room temperature.

These elements are also known as the ....

As you go DOWN Group 0, the boiling point ....

$^{4}_{2}$He
$^{20}_{10}$Ne
$^{40}_{18}$Ar
$^{84}_{36}$Kr
$^{131}_{54}$Xe
$^{222}_{86}$Rn

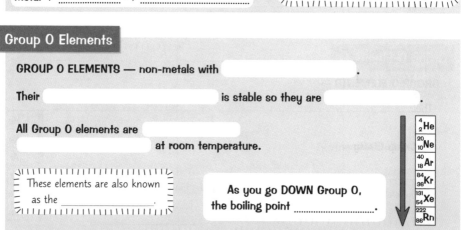

Topic C1 — Atomic Structure and the Periodic Table

124

Group 1 and Group 0 Elements

Trends in Group 1

_____ — common name

for the _____ .

As you go .... :	

$^{7}_{3}$ Li
$^{23}_{11}$ Na
$^{39}_{19}$ K
$^{85}_{37}$ Rb
$^{133}_{55}$ Cs
$^{223}_{87}$ Fr

Properties of Group 1 Metals

_____

They're much _____ .

They're less _____ .

They have lower _____ .

Reactions of Group 1 Elements

The Group 1 elements

They react with

metal + ... → .... + ...

metal + ... → ....

metal + ... → ....

Group 0 Elements

GROUP 0 ELEMENTS — _____ .

Their

All Group 0 elements

These elements are also known as the _____ .

$^{4}_{2}$ He
$^{20}_{10}$ Ne
$^{40}_{18}$ Ar
$^{84}_{36}$ Kr
$^{131}_{54}$ Xe
$^{222}_{86}$ Rn

As you .... ,

....

....

Group 7 Elements

Trends in Group 7

GROUP 7 ELEMENTS — non-metals known as _____.

Halogen		Chlorine	Bromine	
Appearance	yellow gas	.... gas	volatile red-brown	dark grey solid or purple vapour

As you go .... Group 7:		
	decreases	
Melting and boiling points		
		increases

$^{19}_{9}$F	
$^{35.5}_{17}$Cl	
$^{80}_{35}$Br	
$^{127}_{53}$I	
$^{210}_{85}$At	

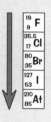

The halogens exist as _____ — _____ two atoms joined by a _____ bond.

Reactions of Group 7 Elements

Halogens have _____ —
they need _____ to be filled.

They can react to fill their outer shell in two ways:

1 _____

Halogens form _____ with other _____ to form molecular compounds.

2 _____

- Halogens form _____ when they react with _____.

- As they gain _____, they form 1– ions called _____.

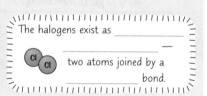

_____ halogens can displace _____ ones.

E.g. _____ + 2KBr$_{(aq)}$ → _____ + 2KCl$_{(aq)}$ ⬅ _____ is more reactive than _____ so displaces it from the salt.

Group 7 Elements

Trends in Group 7

GROUP 7 ELEMENTS — _____.

Halogen			Bromine	
Appearance	yellow gas			

As you go DOWN Group 7:	

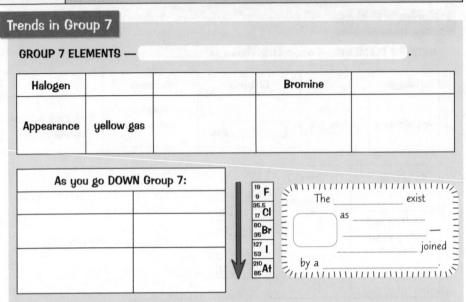

$_9^{19}$F	
$_{17}^{35.5}$Cl	
$_{35}^{80}$Br	
$_{53}^{127}$I	
$_{85}^{210}$At	

The _____ exist as _____ —
_____ joined by a _____.

Reactions of Group 7 Elements

Halogens have _____

They can _____:

1 _____

Halogens form _____

2 _____

• Halogens form _____

• As they gain _____

_____

E.g. _____ + 2 _____(aq) → _____ + 2 _____(aq)

_____ is more reactive than _____

_____
_____

Topic C1 — Atomic Structure and the Periodic Table

Mixed Practice Quizzes

Now, a good chemist likes to do a quiz periodically. Helpfully, here are four practice ones covering the different properties of elements from p.119-126.

Quiz 1 Date: ...... / ...... / ......

1) Describe the typical appearance of a metal.
2) True or false? Group 1 metals are denser than most other metals.
3) Describe the appearance of fluorine gas.
4) How are the elements ordered in the modern periodic table?
5) How does reactivity change as you go down Group 1?
6) What does an element's period number tell you about its electronic structure?
7) What are the Group 0 elements also known as?
8) How many atoms make up a halogen molecule?
9) What is the charge on the ions formed by atoms of Group 1 elements?
10) Which discovery explained why elements cannot be strictly ordered by atomic weight to fit in the Periodic Table?

Total:

Quiz 2 Date: ...... / ...... / ......

1) How many electrons are in the outer shell of a halogen atom?
2) What type of elements react to form positive ions?
3) How do the melting points of Group 1 metals compare to the melting points of most other metals?
4) Which halogen is a dark grey solid?
5) Describe the electrical and thermal conductivity of non-metals.
6) How were elements ordered before the discovery of atomic structure?
7) Give one way that halogens can react to fill their outer electron shell.
8) Why did Mendeleev leave gaps in his Table of Elements?
9) What is an alternative name for the Group 1 metals?
10) What type of compound is formed when a metal reacts with a halogen?

Total:

Mixed Practice Quizzes

Quiz 3   Date: ...... / ...... / ......

1) Give two general properties of non-metals.

2) True or false? Metals are better electrical conductors than most non-metals.

3) Give the word equation for the reaction of a Group 1 metal with chlorine.

4) How does the relative molecular mass of the elements change as you go down Group 7?

5) Where are non-metals found in the Periodic Table?

6) True or false? Non-metals normally react by gaining or sharing electrons.

7) Describe the reactivity of the Group 0 elements.

8) True or false? Non-metals typically have high boiling points.

9) Do the Group 0 elements exist as solids, liquids or gases at room temperature?

10) What is shown by an element's group number?

Total:

Quiz 4   Date: ...... / ...... / ......

1) How did Mendeleev group elements in his Table of Elements?

2) True or false? The more easily a metal loses electrons, the more reactive it is.

3) What is produced when a Group 1 metal reacts with water?

4) Where in the periodic table would you find the most reactive metals?

5) Compare the typical strengths of metals and non-metals.

6) Give the product of the reaction between an alkali metal and oxygen.

7) What happens to the boiling point of the Group 0 elements as you go down the group?

8) True or false? Bromine can displace chlorine from an aqueous solution of its salt.

9) Why are the noble gases unreactive?

10) What name is given to the horizontal rows of the periodic table?

Total:

Topic C1 — Atomic Structure and the Periodic Table

Ions and Ionic Bonding

First Go:
..... / ..... / .....

Ion Formation

IONS — [blank] made when [blank] are transferred.

	Electron transfer	Group	Charge of ion
metals	[blank] electrons (form [blank] ions)		
		2	
non-metals	[blank] electrons (form [blank] ions)	6	
			1–

The [blank] formed by [blank] [blank] have the electronic structure of [blank].

Ionic Bonding

IONIC BONDING — [blank] between [blank] ions. Ionic bonding occurs between [blank] metal ions and [blank] non-metal ions.

Sodium Chloride

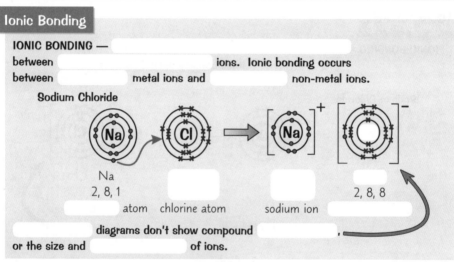

Na
2, 8, 1

[blank] atom   chlorine atom   sodium ion   [blank]

2, 8, 8

[blank] diagrams don't show compound [blank]. or the size and [blank] of ions.

Three Properties of Ionic Compounds

1 Giant ionic lattice structure — [blank] of attraction between oppositely charged ions act [blank].

2 High [blank] points — lots of energy needed to [blank].

3 Conduct electricity only when [blank] — ions free to move and [blank].

Limitations:
• Model not [blank]
• In reality, no [blank] between ions

Limitation: can only see [blank] of compound.

[blank] of ionic compounds can be worked out from diagrams.

Ions and Ionic Bonding

Ion Formation

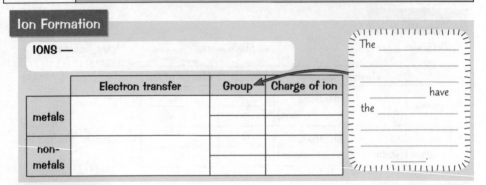

IONS —

	Electron transfer	Group	Charge of ion
metals			
non-metals			

The .... have the ....

Ionic Bonding

IONIC BONDING — .... Ionic bonding occurs between ....

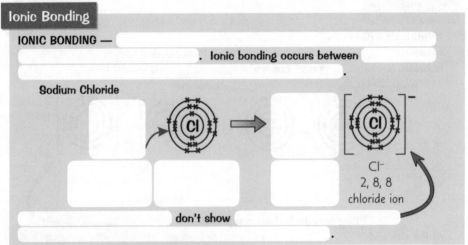

Sodium Chloride

Cl⁻
2, 8, 8
chloride ion

don't show

Three Properties of Ionic Compounds

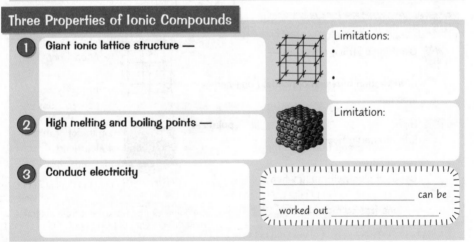

1 Giant ionic lattice structure —

Limitations:
•
•

2 High melting and boiling points —

Limitation:

3 Conduct electricity

.... can be worked out ....

Covalent Bonding & Simple Molecules

Covalent Bonding

COVALENT BOND — a [____] pair of electrons between two [____].
Covalent bonding happens in non-metal [____] and in non-metal [____].

Molecular formulas show you [____] of each **NH₃**
element are in [____].

Dot and cross diagrams don't show [____] of atoms or their [____] in space.

Ball and stick diagrams don't show [____] the electrons in [____] come from.

H
|
H—N—H

Displayed formula — doesn't show [____].

Simple Molecular Substances

Covalent bonds between [____] are [____].
Forces between [____] are [____].

Elements

[____] (H₂)   [____]   Nitrogen [____]   Chlorine (Cl₂)

Compounds

Hydrogen Chloride (HCl)   Water [____]   [____]   Methane [____]

Two Properties of Simple Molecular Substances

1. Low melting and boiling points — mostly [____] at [____].

2. Don't conduct electricity — there are [____] particles to [____].

As molecules get [____], less energy is needed to [____] between them.

 ☑   ☑   ☑   Topic C2 — Bonding, Structure and Properties of Matter

Covalent Bonding & Simple Molecules

Covalent Bonding

COVALENT BOND —

Molecular formulas show

NH_3

Ball and stick diagrams

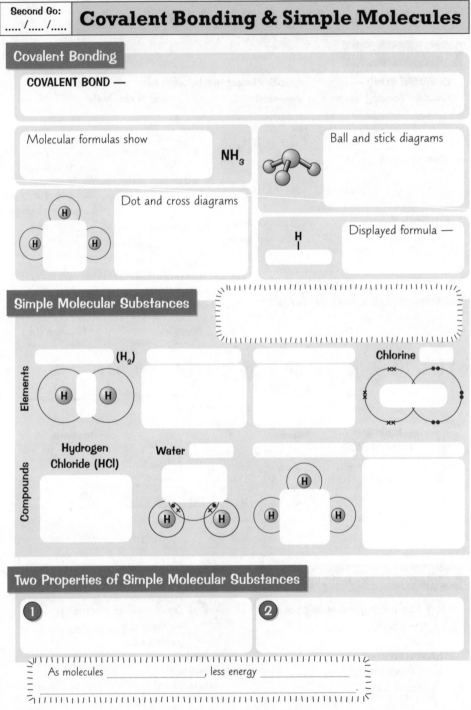

Dot and cross diagrams

H
|

Displayed formula —

Simple Molecular Substances

Elements

(H_2)

Chlorine

Compounds

Hydrogen
Chloride (HCl)

Water

Two Properties of Simple Molecular Substances

1

2

As molecules _____, less energy _____

Topic C2 — Bonding, Structure and Properties of Matter ☑ ☑ ☑

Covalent Structures

Polymers

POLYMERS — very long [____] of [_____].

They're usually [____] at room temperature because they have [_____].

$$\left(\begin{array}{cc} H & H \\ | & | \\ -C-C- \\ | & | \\ H & H \end{array}\right)_n$$

strong [_____] bonds

'n' is a large [____]

Giant Covalent Structures

GIANT COVALENT STRUCTURES — [_____] containing atoms which are [____] by [_____] covalent bonds.

High melting and boiling points — [_____] to overcome [_____] covalent bonds.

Don't conduct [_____] (with a couple of exceptions) — no [_____] to carry charge.

Examples include: _____, graphite and _____ (silica).

Useful in _____ and composites.

Carbon Allotropes

	Diamond	Graphite	Graphene
Bonding	C atoms form [____] covalent bonds	C atoms form [____] covalent bonds. No covalent bonds between [____]	C atoms form [____] covalent bonds
Properties	Very [____]	Soft, [____]	[____], light
Melting Point	High	[____]	
Conductivity	Doesn't conduct [____]	Conducts electricity and [____] energy	[____] electricity

Each carbon atom in graphite and graphene has [_____] electron.

FULLERENES — have [_____] shapes. rings of [____] (sometimes 5 or 7)

Buckminsterfullerene ([__]) is [_____] and was the first to be discovered.

NANOTUBES — [_____] fullerenes used in nanotechnology, [_____] and materials. They have high [_____] ratios.

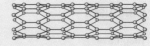

Covalent Structures

Polymers

POLYMERS —

They're usually

strong

'n' is ....

Giant Covalent Structures

GIANT COVALENT STRUCTURES —

High melting and

Don't conduct

Examples include: ....
....

Useful in ....
....

Carbon Allotropes

Bonding	C atoms form	C atoms form	C atoms form
Properties			
Melting Point			
Conductivity			

Each carbon atom in

FULLERENES —

rings of

Buckminsterfullerene

and was the first to be discovered.

NANOTUBES —

They have

Metallic Bonding

Metallic Bonding

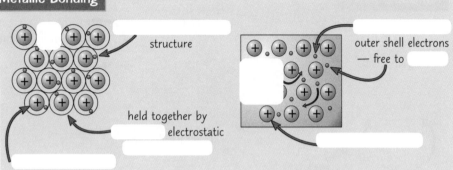

structure

outer shell electrons
— free to

held together by
                    electrostatic

Four Properties of Metals

1. High melting and boiling points — lots of [____] needed to overcome [____].

2. Good thermal conductors — energy [____] by [____] electrons.

3. Good electrical conductors — [____].

4. Soft and malleable — layers in metals [____].

Alloys

ALLOYS — a [____] of a metal and at least [____].

Alloys are [____] than pure metals.

New element [____] layers of metal atoms — they can't [____].

Metallic Bonding

Metallic Bonding

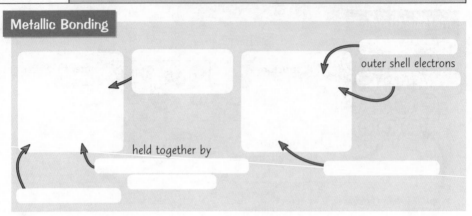

outer shell electrons

held together by

Four Properties of Metals

1. High _____ — lots of energy needed _____.

2. Good _____ conductors — _____ by _____.

3. Good _____ conductors — _____ _____.

4. Soft and malleable — _____ _____.

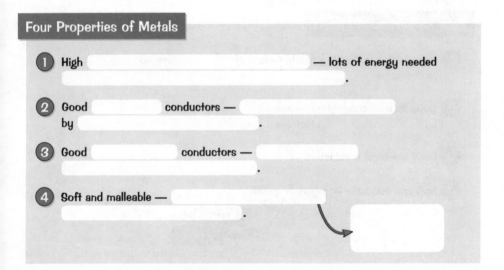

Alloys

ALLOYS — _____

New element

Alloys are _____ .

Topic C2 — Bonding, Structure and Properties of Matter

States of Matter and Changing State

Particle Theory

	Solid		Gas
Particle Diagram	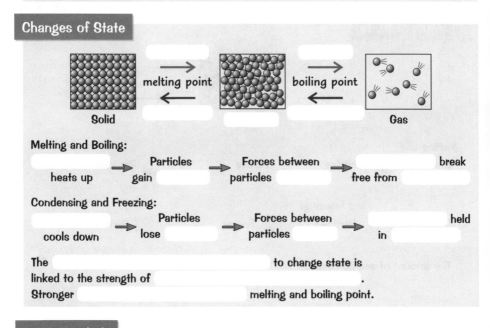		
Particle Arrangement			Random
Particle Movement	Fixed position, vibrate		Move in all ___
Particle Closeness	___ close together		

Atoms don't have the ___ properties of ___.

Changes of State

| Solid | ___ | melting point | ___ | boiling point | Gas |

Melting and Boiling:

___ heats up → Particles gain ___ → Forces between particles ___ → ___ break free from ___

Condensing and Freezing:

___ cools down → Particles lose ___ → Forces between particles ___ → ___ held in ___

The ___ to change state is linked to the strength of ___.

Stronger ___ melting and boiling point.

State Symbols

	(l)		(aq)
solid			

 ✓   ✓   ✓ Topic C2 — Bonding, Structure and Properties of Matter

Second Go: ...... /...... /...... States of Matter and Changing State

Particle Theory

Particle Diagram		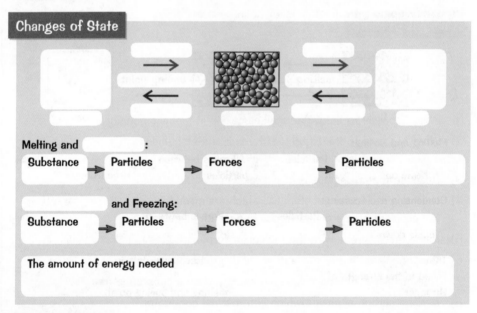	
Particle Arrangement			
Particle Movement			
Particle Closeness			

Atoms don't _____.

Changes of State

	→		→	
	←		←	

Melting and _____ :

Substance → Particles → Forces → Particles

_____ and Freezing:

Substance → Particles → Forces → Particles

The amount of energy needed

State Symbols

Topic C2 — Bonding, Structure and Properties of Matter

Mixed Practice Quizzes

Hope you've got your head round all those state changes, because it's quiz time. These four will test you on the information covered on p.129-138. Let's get to it.

Quiz 1 | Date: ...... / ...... / ......

1) Which type of bonding occurs between a metal and a non-metal?

2) Give one property of substances with giant covalent structures.

3) Which state of matter contains a regular arrangement of particles?

4) What is meant by the term 'alloy'?

5) What do the shapes of fullerenes have in common?

6) Why can simple molecular substances not conduct electricity?

7) Describe the dot and cross structure of a hydrogen molecule.

8) What is the state symbol for a liquid?

9) Why do metals have high boiling points?

10) What type of attraction is involved in ionic bonding?

Total:

Quiz 2 | Date: ...... / ...... / ......

1) What happens to the outer shell electrons in metallic bonding?

2) What happens to the layers of atoms in a metal when a new element is added to form an alloy?

3) Describe the arrangement of particles in a liquid.

4) In simple molecular substances, which are stronger — the covalent bonds or the forces between molecules?

5) Name the fullerene with the molecular formula C_{60}.

6) Give one limitation of dot and cross diagrams.

7) True or false? The particles gain energy when a substance freezes.

8) Name a carbon allotrope which is a thermal conductor.

9) Describe what a polymer is.

10) Do metals lose electrons or gain electrons in order to form ions?

Total:

Topic C2 — Bonding, Structure and Properties of Matter

Mixed Practice Quizzes

Quiz 3   Date: ...... / ...... / ......

1) Give three examples of giant covalent substances.

2) Why are polymers usually solid at room temperature?

3) Why are alloys harder than pure metals?

4) Explain why metals are good thermal conductors.

5) What states are simple molecular substances usually in
   at room temperature?

6) What does the state symbol (aq) tell you about a substance?

7) Which allotrope is a single layer of covalently bonded carbon atoms?

8) Which state of matter contains vibrating particles that are fixed in position?

9) Give one example of a simple molecular substance.

10) What name is given to a shared pair of electrons between
    two non-metal atoms?

Total:

Quiz 4   Date: ...... / ...... / ......

1) When a substance condenses, do the particles gain energy or lose energy?

2) Name one carbon allotrope that does not conduct electricity.

3) True or false? Metals melt at very low temperatures.

4) What type of attraction holds a metallic structure together?

5) How many electrons are shared between the two atoms in
   a nitrogen molecule?

6) In which states will ionic compounds conduct electricity?

7) What type of bonding occurs in sodium chloride?

8) True or false? Nanotubes have low length to diameter ratios.

9) Which state of matter consists of particles that are close together
   but are moving round each other?

10) Which type of diagram should you use if you want to show
    the 3D structure of a molecule?

Total:

Mass and Concentration

First Go:
..... / ..... / .....

Relative Formula Mass

RELATIVE FORMULA MASS ( ) — sum of [_____]
[_____] of the atoms in the [_____].

Percentage mass of
[_____]
= $\dfrac{\text{[_____]}}{\text{[_____]}}$ × [____]

Balanced Equations

BALANCED EQUATION — [_____]
equation with [_____]
of atoms of each element
on [_____].

....Mg + O$_2$ → ....MgO

In a [_____]:

Sum of the [____]
of the [____] = Sum of the [____]
of the [____]
[____] [____]

Concentration

CONCENTRATION — amount of
.... dissolved in a certain
....

[____]
of solute
( ) = $\dfrac{\text{concentration}}{(\ /dm^3)}$ × [____]
of solvent
(dm^3)

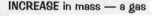

For .... measurements, the
.... of the results can be used to find
the .... in the mean value.

Conservation of Mass

No atoms are [_____] in a [_____] reaction, so the total
masses of reactants and products are also [_____] — MASS IS [_____].

If you weigh an [_____] reaction vessel, sometimes you'll see a [_____]:

DECREASE in mass — a gas [_____]
during the reaction and [_____] the
vessel, so its mass is [_____]
[_____].

INCREASE in mass — a gas [_____]
[_____], so its mass
is [_____] the mass in the vessel
(none of the [_____] are gaseous).

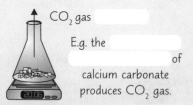

CO$_2$ gas [_____]

E.g. the [_____]
[_____] of
calcium carbonate
produces CO$_2$ gas.

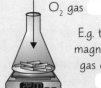

O$_2$ gas [_____]

E.g. the reaction of
magnesium with O$_2$
gas only produces
[_____].

Mass and Concentration

Relative Formula Mass

RELATIVE FORMULA MASS ( ) —

Percentage mass of

=

Balanced Equations

BALANCED EQUATION —

.....Mg + O_2 → ....

In a :

=

Concentration

CONCENTRATION —

$\dfrac{\text{mass of solute}}{(\ )}$ =

For _____ ,
the _____
can be used to find the _____
_____ .

Conservation of Mass

No atoms

If you

DECREASE in mass —

INCREASE in mass —

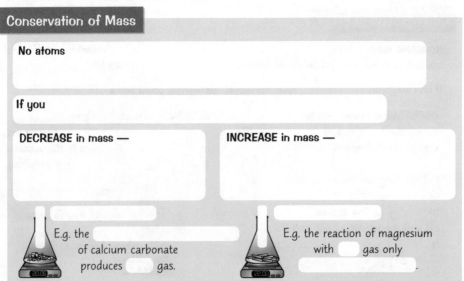

E.g. the _____
of calcium carbonate
produces ____ gas.

E.g. the reaction of magnesium
with ____ gas only
_____ .

 ☑ ☑ ☑

Acids, Bases and their Reactions

First Go:
..... / ..... / .....

The pH Scale

Alkalis are _____ bases.

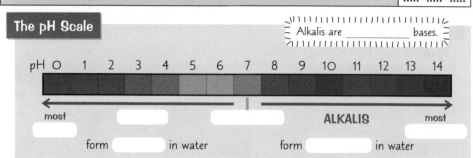

pH 0 1 2 3 4 5 6 7 8 9 10 11 12 13 14

most [____] [____] [____] **ALKALIS** most [____]

form [____] in water   form [____] in water

Two Ways to Measure pH

1. **UNIVERSAL INDICATOR** — a wide range [____] [____] depending on [____]. It gives [____] pH value.

2. **pH PROBE** — gives [____] of the pH.

Neutralisation Reactions

.... + base ➡ salt + ...

The products of neutralisation reactions are [____].

.... + OH⁻(aq) ➡ ....

Reactions of Acids

To get the formula of a salt, _____ the charges of the ions so the _____ is _____.

acid + [____] ➡ salt + [____] + carbon dioxide

acid + metal oxide ➡ [____] + [____]

acid + metal hydroxide ➡ [____] + [____]

Soluble salts are made by adding [____] or [____] to [____]. The excess [____] is filtered off and the remaining salt solution is [____].

Acid Used	Salt Produced
HCl	
H₂SO₄	
HNO₃	

The first part of a salt's name comes from [____] in the base, alkali or carbonate.

Second Go:
...... / ...... / ......

Acids, Bases and their Reactions

The pH Scale

Alkalis are _____.

pH O 1 2 3 4 5 6 7 8 9 10 11 12 13 14

form _____   form _____

Two Ways to Measure pH

1 **UNIVERSAL INDICATOR —**

It gives

2 **pH PROBE —**

Neutralisation Reactions

.... + ... ➡ .... + ...

The products of _____

_____.

.... + ... ➡ ....

Reactions of Acids

To get the

acid + _____ ➡ salt + _____ + _____

acid + _____ ➡ _____

acid + _____ ➡ _____

Soluble salts

The excess

Acid Used	Salt Produced
H_2SO_4	

The first part of

Reactivity of Metals

The Reactivity Series

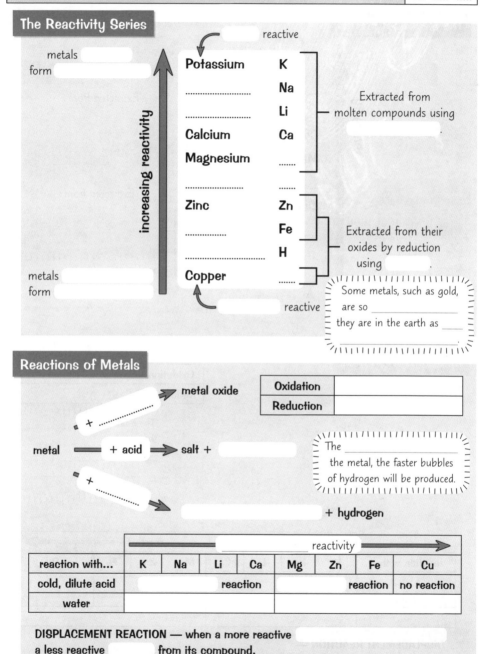

.... reactive

metals [........]
form [..................]

increasing reactivity

Potassium — **K**
.... **Na**
.... **Li**
Calcium **Ca**
Magnesium ....

Extracted from molten compounds using [..................].

....
Zinc **Zn**
.... **Fe**
.... **H**
Copper ....

Extracted from their oxides by reduction using [..........].

.... reactive

Some metals, such as gold, are so .... they are in the earth as ....

metals [..................]
form [..................]

Reactions of Metals

metal oxide

Oxidation	
Reduction	

[........] + ... ➔ metal oxide

metal ➔ + acid ➔ salt + [..................]

The .... the metal, the faster bubbles of hydrogen will be produced.

+ .... ➔ [..................] + hydrogen

reaction with...	K	Na	Li	Ca	Mg	Zn	Fe	Cu
cold, dilute acid	reaction					reaction		no reaction
water								

.... reactivity ➔

DISPLACEMENT REACTION — when a more reactive [..................] a less reactive [........] from its compound.

 ☑ ☑ ☑

Topic C4 — Chemical Changes

Reactivity of Metals

The Reactivity Series

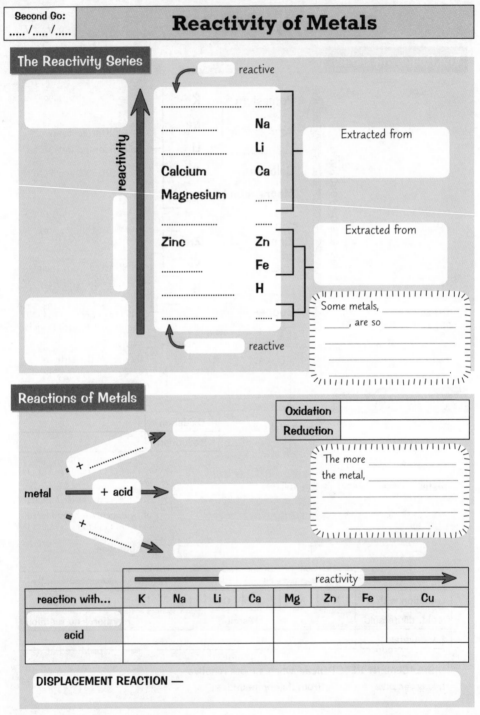

.... reactive

....
.... **Na**
.... **Li**
Calcium **Ca**
Magnesium ....

reactivity

Extracted from

....
Zinc **Zn**
.... **Fe**
.... **H**
....

Extracted from

Some metals, _____
_____, are so _____
_____
_____
_____.

.... reactive

Reactions of Metals

| Oxidation | |
| Reduction | |

The more _____
the metal, _____
_____
_____.

metal ——— + acid ——→

+ ....

+ ....

reactivity

reaction with...	K	Na	Li	Ca	Mg	Zn	Fe	Cu
acid								

DISPLACEMENT REACTION —

Topic C4 — Chemical Changes

Electrolysis

Electrolysis of Molten Ionic Compounds

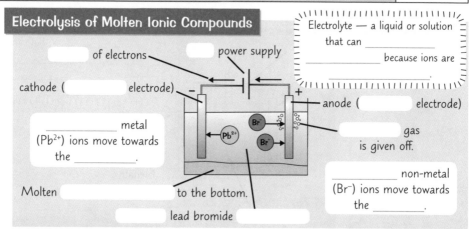

Electrolyte — a liquid or solution that can _____ _____ because ions are _____.

_____ of electrons

power supply

cathode (_____ electrode) −

anode (_____ electrode)

_____ metal (Pb^{2+}) ions move towards the _____.

_____ gas is given off.

Molten _____ to the bottom.

_____ non-metal (Br^-) ions move towards the _____.

lead bromide

Extraction of Aluminium

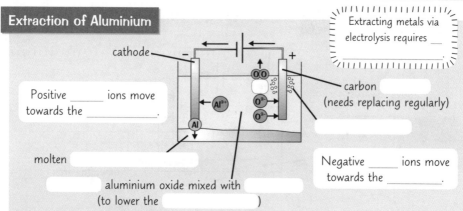

Extracting metals via electrolysis requires _____ _____.

cathode −

carbon _____ (needs replacing regularly)

Positive _____ ions move towards the _____.

molten _____

aluminium oxide mixed with _____ (to lower the _____)

Negative _____ ions move towards the _____.

Electrolysis of Aqueous Ionic Compounds

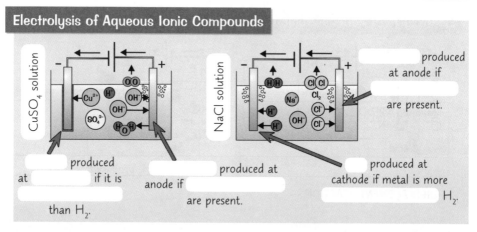

$CuSO_4$ solution

NaCl solution

_____ produced at anode if _____ are present.

_____ produced at _____ if it is _____ than H_2.

_____ produced at anode if _____ are present.

_____ produced at cathode if metal is more _____ H_2.

Topic C4 — Chemical Changes

Electrolysis

Electrolysis of Molten Ionic Compounds

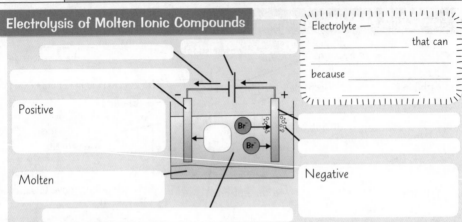

Positive

Molten

Electrolyte — _____ that can

_____

because _____

Negative

Extraction of Aluminium

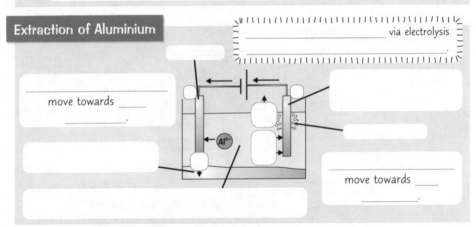

_____ via electrolysis

move towards _____

move towards _____

Electrolysis of Aqueous Ionic Compounds

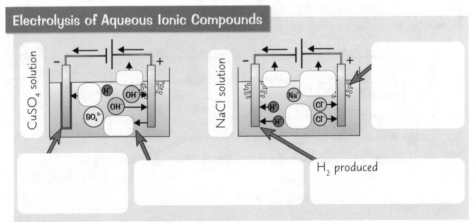

$CuSO_4$ solution

NaCl solution

H_2 produced

Topic C4 — Chemical Changes

Mixed Practice Quizzes

Here are some quick-fire quiz questions to test what you've done on p.141-148.
No, honestly, you're welcome. Mark each test yourself and tot up your score.

Quiz 1   Date: ...... / ...... / ......

1) What name is given to a base that is soluble in water?
2) What ions are produced when an acid ionises in water?
3) Give one unit used to measure concentration.
4) Why might the mass of a reaction vessel decrease during a reaction?
5) How is a reactive metal such as potassium extracted from a compound?
6) What is produced when a metal reacts with water?
7) Is reduction the gain or loss of oxygen?
8) What is the definition of 'relative formula mass'?
9) Explain what is meant by the term 'electrolyte'.
10) What is produced at the anode during the extraction of aluminium?

Total:

Quiz 2   Date: ...... / ...... / ......

1) What is the pH of a neutral solution?
2) Give two ways of measuring the pH of a solution.
3) What is produced by the reaction of an acid and a metal oxide?
4) True or false? The range of a set of results can be used to find the uncertainty in the mean value.
5) What is meant by the term 'balanced equation'?
6) True or false? Unreactive metals readily form positive ions.
7) True or false? The reaction between lithium and cold dilute acid is moderate.
8) What does 'conservation of mass' mean?
9) What name is given to the negative electrode in electrolysis?
10) What material is used to make the anode in aluminium extraction?

Total:

Topic C4 — Chemical Changes

Mixed Practice Quizzes

Quiz 3   Date: ...... / ...... / ......

1) True or false? Universal indicator gives an exact pH value.   ☑

2) Which ions react in a neutralisation reaction between an acid and a base?   ☑

3) Which type of salt is produced when HNO_3 reacts with a metal carbonate?   ☑

4) Compare the total M_rs of the reactants and products in a balanced equation.   ☑

5) Give an equation used to calculate the mass of solute in a solution.   ☑

6) How is iron extracted from iron oxide?   ☑

7) Describe what occurs during a displacement reaction.   ☑

8) What term is given to the sum of the relative atomic masses in a formula?   ☑

9) What is produced at the cathode during the electrolysis of molten lead bromide?   ☑

10) What determines whether hydrogen gas is produced at the cathode during the electrolysis of an aqueous ionic compound?   ☑

Total: ⬜

Quiz 4   Date: ...... / ...... / ......

1) Give a method of producing soluble salts.   ☑

2) Give two examples of metals which react with water and react explosively with cold, dilute acid.   ☑

3) What can be reacted with an acid to produce carbon dioxide?   ☑

4) How would the mass of a reaction vessel change if a gaseous reactant from the air takes part in the reaction?   ☑

5) True or false? Calcium is less reactive than zinc.   ☑

6) Name a metal that does not react with either acid or water.   ☑

7) Give a definition of the term 'concentration'.   ☑

8) Give an equation that could be used to work out the percentage mass of an element in a compound.   ☑

9) What is mixed with molten aluminium oxide to lower the melting point?   ☑

10) What substances are produced at the anode during the electrolysis of an aqueous ionic compound if no halide ions are present?   ☑

Total: ⬜

Endothermic & Exothermic Reactions

Energy Transfer

Energy is [   ] in chemical reactions. After a reaction, the [   ] amount of energy in the universe is [   ].

ENDOTHERMIC reaction:

[   ] energy from the surroundings — shown by a [   ] in temperature.

Reactions include:

* [   ]

* Citric acid + sodium hydrogencarbonate

Use: some [   ] packs

EXOTHERMIC reaction:

[   ] energy to the surroundings — shown by a [   ] in temperature.

Reactions include:

* [   ]

* Neutralisation

* Most [   ] reactions

Uses: self-heating cans and [   ]

Reaction Profiles

ENDOTHERMIC

Energy

Activation energy

Products

Reactants

Progress of Reaction

[   ]

Energy

Activation energy

Progress of Reaction

ACTIVATION ENERGY (E_a) — [   ]
of energy that reactants [   ].

Second Go:
...... / ...... / ......

Endothermic & Exothermic Reactions

Energy Transfer

Energy is _____ .
After a reaction, _____
_____ .

_____ reaction:

Takes in energy

Reactions include:

Use: some _____

EXOTHERMIC reaction:

Transfers energy

Reactions include:

Uses:

Reaction Profiles

<u>ENDOTHERMIC</u>

Activation energy

Products

Reactants

ACTIVATION ENERGY (E$_a$) —

Rates of Reaction

Comparing Rates of Reaction

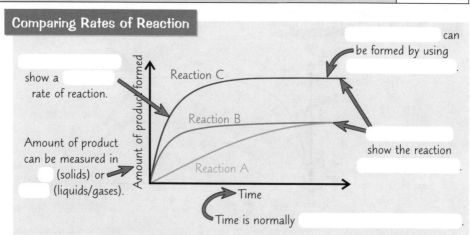

[blank] show a [blank] rate of reaction.

Amount of product can be measured in [blank] (solids) or [blank] (liquids/gases).

[blank] can be formed by using [blank].

[blank] show the reaction [blank]

Time is normally [blank]

Measuring Rates of Reaction

$$\text{Mean rate of reaction} = \frac{\dotfill}{\text{Time}} \quad \text{or} \quad \frac{\dotfill}{\text{Time}}$$

Units depend on [blank] — they're in the form [blank].

Two common [blank] : g/s [blank]

Using Rate Graphs

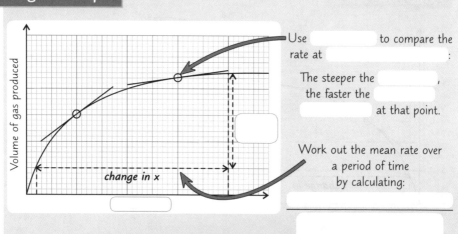

Use [blank] to compare the rate at [blank]:

The steeper the [blank], the faster the [blank] at that point.

Work out the mean rate over a period of time by calculating:

[blank]

change in x

Second Go:
..... / ..... / .....

Rates of Reaction

Comparing Rates of Reaction

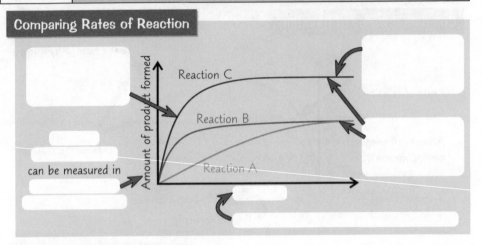

can be measured in

Measuring Rates of Reaction

Mean rate = ... or ....
of reaction   ....

Units depend on
— they're in the form

:

Using Rate Graphs

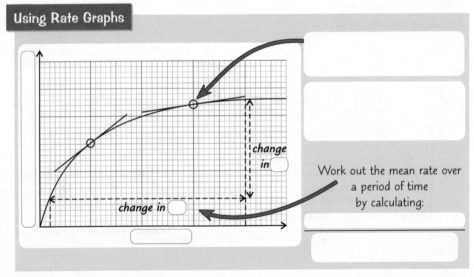

change
in

change in

Work out the mean rate over
a period of time
by calculating:

Collision Theory and Catalysts

Collision Theory

High
High
Fast

Low
Low
Slow

The rate of a chemical reaction depends on...

Collision frequency — the [_____] between particles, the [_____] the rate of reaction. So doubling the frequency of [_____] would [_____] the rate.

Collision energy — [_____] energy needs to be transferred in a collision to overcome the [_____] and [_____] to start the reaction.

The minimum energy particles need to react is called the _____.

Catalysts

CATALYSTS — [_____] reactions without being used up by providing an [_____] for the reaction. Different reactions need [_____].

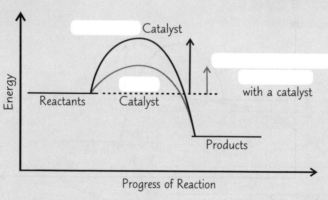

Catalyst

Reactants   Catalyst

Products

Energy

Progress of Reaction

with a catalyst

Enzymes are _____ catalysts.

     Topic C6 — The Rate and Extent of Chemical Change

Collision Theory and Catalysts

Collision Theory

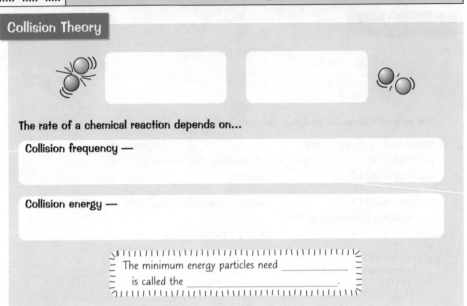

The rate of a chemical reaction depends on...

Collision frequency —

Collision energy —

The minimum energy particles need _____
is called the _____.

Catalysts

CATALYSTS —

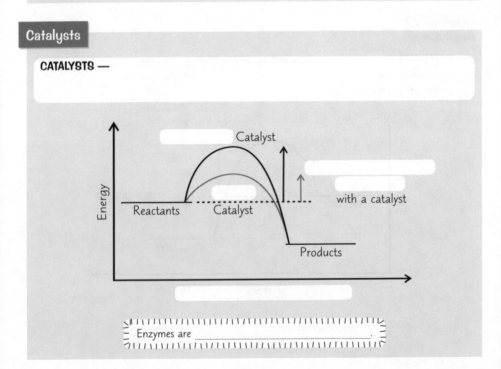

Enzymes are _____.

Topic C6 — The Rate and Extent of Chemical Change

Factors Affecting Rates of Reaction

Temperature

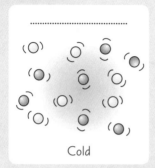

Cold

Particles [_____] and collide more [_____] with more energy.

Pressure or Concentration

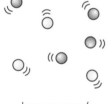

Low pressure/ concentration

SLOW RATE

High pressure/ concentration

FAST RATE

[_____] in the same [_____] — more [_____].

Surface Area

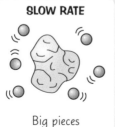

Big pieces

SLOW RATE

Small pieces

FAST RATE

[_____] for particles to [_____] with — more [_____] collisions.

The _____ the piece of solid, the larger the _____ _____ ratio.

 ☑ ☑ ☑   **Topic C6 — The Rate and Extent of Chemical Change**

Factors Affecting Rates of Reaction

Temperature

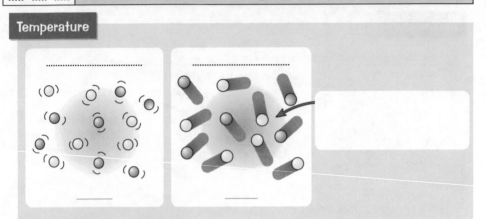

Pressure or Concentration

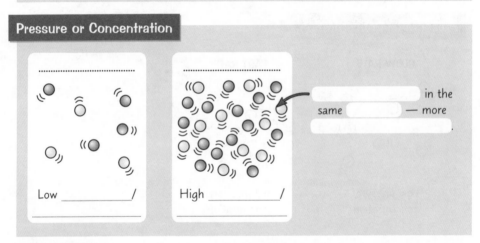

_____ in the

same _____ — more

_____

Low _____ /

High _____ /

Surface Area

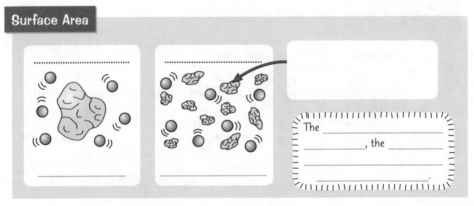

The

_____, the _____

_____

_____.

Topic C6 — The Rate and Extent of Chemical Change

Reversible Reactions

Equilibrium

Equilibrium can only be reached when a ....
takes place in a .... (where nothing can enter or leave).

$$A + B \rightleftharpoons C + D$$

....
.... —
where the products
can react to form
....
....

A
B
Forward Reaction
C
D

Same rate

At equilibrium, the
....
of reactants and products
....

A
B
Backward Reaction
C
D

.... :
the equilibrium lies
to the ....

.... :
the equilibrium lies
to the ....

Changing Reaction Conditions

Changing reaction conditions can change the
....

.... the
reaction favours
the left.

ammonium chloride $\rightleftharpoons$ ammonia + hydrogen chloride

.... the
reaction favours
the right.

Exothermic and Endothermic Reactions

If the reaction is .... in one direction, it will be .... in the other.

Hydrated copper sulfate $\rightleftharpoons$ Anhydrous copper sulfate + Water

The .... is transferred in each direction.

   Topic C6 — The Rate and Extent of Chemical Change

Reversible Reactions

Equilibrium

Equilibrium can only be reached

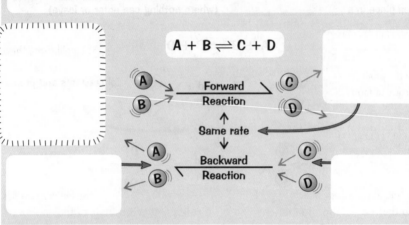

$$A + B \rightleftharpoons C + D$$

Forward Reaction

A
B

C
D

Same rate

Backward Reaction

A
B

C
D

Changing Reaction Conditions

Changing reaction

ammonium chloride $\rightleftharpoons$ ammonia + hydrogen chloride

Exothermic and Endothermic Reactions

If the reaction is

Hydrated copper sulfate _____ Anhydrous copper sulfate + Water

Topic C6 — The Rate and Extent of Chemical Change

Mixed Practice Quizzes

Time to increase your rate of revision by throwing in a quiz catalyst. All of these questions are based on p.151-160, so make sure you've gone over those first.

Quiz 1   Date: ...... / ...... / ......

1) Give an example of a unit used to measure the rate of a reaction.
2) How does heating a substance affect the movement of its particles?
3) How is the energy released by an exothermic reaction shown on a reaction profile?
4) How can you tell from a rate graph when a reaction is finished?
5) What is meant by the term 'activation energy'?
6) What effect will doubling the collision frequency have on the rate?
7) What type of reaction takes in energy from the surroundings?
8) How does a catalyst affect the activation energy of a reaction?
9) True or false? The steeper the line on a rate graph, the faster the reaction.
10) How would you find the rate at a specific point on a rate graph?

Total:

Quiz 2   Date: ...... / ...... / ......

1) What does it mean if a reaction is reversible?
2) What is represented by the horizontal axis on a rate graph?
3) How does decreasing the concentration of reactants in solution affect the rate of reaction?
4) What are biological catalysts called?
5) True or false? The concentrations of reactants don't change at equilibrium.
6) Does the overall energy of the universe change after a reaction?
7) True or false? All reactions can use the same catalysts.
8) According to collision theory, which two factors determine the rate of a reaction?
9) In the reaction profile for an endothermic reaction, are the reactants or products at higher energy?
10) Give an example of a product that uses an exothermic reaction.

Total:

Topic C6 — The Rate and Extent of Chemical Change

Mixed Practice Quizzes

Quiz 3   Date: ...... / ...... / ......

1) True or false? Equilibrium can be only reached in an open system.

2) Can a reversible reaction be endothermic in both directions?

3) How does increasing the concentration of the particles in a reaction affect the collision frequency?

4) How would you work out the mean rate of reaction over a period of time?

5) Give two examples of types of reaction that are exothermic.

6) How can you tell which reaction shown on a single graph has the fastest rate?

7) Why does increasing the surface area of a reactant increase reaction rate?

8) True or false? Changing the temperature of a reversible reaction can change the direction of the reaction.

9) How do catalysts speed up reactions?

10) What is represented on the horizontal axis of a reaction profile?

Total:

Quiz 4   Date: ...... / ...... / ......

1) What's the minimum amount of energy that reactants need to react called?

2) What is meant by a closed system?

3) What can you say about the rates of the forward and backward reactions of a reversible reaction at equilibrium?

4) True or false? Mean rate of reaction = amount of reactant used × time

5) Why does a higher pressure mean a faster rate of reaction between gases?

6) True or false? Some sports injury packs use endothermic reactions.

7) If the equilibrium lies to the left, are there more reactants or products at equilibrium?

8) True or false? In an exothermic reaction profile, the products are at a lower energy than the reactants.

9) Which factor affects both collision frequency and collision energy?

10) In which type of reaction does the temperature of the surroundings fall?

Total:

Topic C6 — The Rate and Extent of Chemical Change

Crude Oil and Fractional Distillation

Crude Oil

CRUDE OIL — a mixture of many _____.

_____ only contain hydrogen and carbon atoms.

It's a finite resource found in _____ and formed from _____ _____ that have spent _____ buried in mud.

Crude oil is processed to produce _____ and to provide stock chemicals used _____ polymers, _____, lubricants etc.

Combustion

COMPLETE COMBUSTION — an _____ reaction that occurs when a _____ reacts with plenty of _____.

hydrocarbon + ...

⬇

.... + ...

Hydrocarbons are used as _____ because combustion _____ a lot of energy.

Hydrocarbons

As the length of the hydrocarbon chain increases, the...	
...boiling point _____ .	
... _____ increases.	
...flammability _____ .	

Fractional Distillation

FRACTIONAL DISTILLATION — a process used to _____ the _____ in crude oil into _____ according to _____.

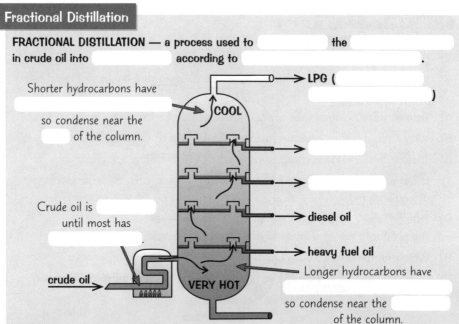

Shorter hydrocarbons have _____ so condense near the _____ of the column.

○ ➤ LPG (_____)

COOL

Crude oil is _____ until most has _____.

crude oil ➤

VERY HOT

➤ _____

➤ _____

➤ diesel oil

➤ heavy fuel oil

Longer hydrocarbons have _____ so condense near the _____ of the column.

 ✓   ✓ ☺ ✓

Crude Oil and Fractional Distillation

Crude Oil

CRUDE OIL —

_____ only contain
_____ .

It's a finite resource

Crude oil is processed to _____
_____ used to manufacture _____ ,
_____ , lubricants etc.

Combustion

COMPLETE COMBUSTION —

.... + ...
⬇
.... + ...

Hydrocarbons are used as _____
_____ .

Hydrocarbons

As the length of the		
_____ , the...		

Fractional Distillation

FRACTIONAL DISTILLATION —

Shorter hydrocarbons

COOL

Crude oil is

VERY HOT

Longer hydrocarbons

Alkanes and Cracking

Alkanes

ALKANES — the _____ type of hydrocarbon, containing only _____ (they're saturated).

Most hydrocarbons in _____ are alkanes.

The general formula for the _____ of alkanes is _____ .

Number of carbon atoms	1	2	3	4
Name	Methane		Propane	
Formula		C_2H_6	C_3H_8	

Structure		H H
		  | |
		H—C—C—H
		  | |
		H H
				H H H H
				 | | | |
				H—C—C—C—C—H
				 | | | |
				H H H H

Two Methods of Cracking

There is _____ for fuels with _____ carbon chains.

CRACKING — breaks down _____ hydrocarbons into

_____ .

_____ -chain alkane ⟹ _____ + alkene

Alkenes are used to make _____ and are _____ for making other chemicals.

Long-chain hydrocarbons are _____ by heating.

Hydrocarbon vapour is passed over a _____

_____ .

Hydrocarbon vapour is mixed with _____ and heated to _____

_____ .

1 _____ cracking   Heat

2 _____ cracking   Heat

Alkenes are _____ than alkanes.

Adding an alkene to _____ causes it to change from _____ .

_____ +
bromine test

 ☑ ☑ ☑

Alkanes and Cracking

Alkanes

ALKANES —

The [   ] for the [   ].

Most hydrocarbons _____.

Number of carbon atoms	1	2	3	4
Name				
Formula				
Structure				

Two Methods of Cracking

There is [   ] for fuels with [   ].

CRACKING —

[   ] ⟶ [   ] + [   ]

Alkenes are used _____

[   ] hydrocarbons are [   ].

Hydrocarbon vapour is [   ]   Hydrocarbon vapour is [   ]

① [   ]   ② [   ]

Alkenes are [   ].

Adding an alkene [   ]

Mixed Practice Quizzes

Hopefully you've cracked all the information on p.163-166, because it's time for some questions. Remember to check how you've done afterwards.

Quiz 1   Date: ...... / ...... / ......

1) What type of hydrocarbon is crude oil mostly made up of?
2) Give the word equation for the complete combustion of a hydrocarbon.
3) Which are more reactive — alkanes or alkenes?
4) Give two examples of products that are made from chemicals produced from crude oil.
5) Why are hydrocarbons used as fuels?
6) What is the purpose of cracking hydrocarbons?
7) Give the name and formula of the alkane with two carbon atoms.
8) How does the chain length of a hydrocarbon affect its boiling point?
9) True or false? The alkenes produced by cracking are only used as fuels.
10) Name two methods of cracking.

Total:

Quiz 2   Date: ...... / ...... / ......

1) What happens to crude oil during fractional distillation?
2) Which two elements make up hydrocarbons?
3) Which method of cracking involves mixing hydrocarbon vapour with another gas and heating to a very high temperature?
4) True or false? When an alkane is cracked, only alkenes are produced.
5) What is crude oil?
6) What would you see if you added an alkene to bromine water?
7) How is the length of the hydrocarbon chain related to viscosity?
8) What are the products of complete combustion of a hydrocarbon fuel?
9) Give three fuels produced from the fractional distillation of crude oil.
10) Where do shorter hydrocarbons condense in a fractionating column?

Total:

Mixed Practice Quizzes

Date: ...... / ...... / ......

1) Are long-chain hydrocarbons more flammable than short-chain hydrocarbons?
2) What is used as the catalyst in catalytic cracking?
3) What is the chemical formula of methane?
4) How many carbon atoms are present in a molecule of propane?
5) What did crude oil form from?
6) True or false? Fractionating columns are hotter at the top than the bottom.
7) What type of chemical bond is found in alkanes?
8) Describe how to test for an alkene.
9) Give one use of alkenes.
10) True or false? There is a high demand for fuels with shorter carbon chains.

Total:

Quiz 4 Date: ...... / ...... / ......

1) What is the name of the alkane with the formula C_4H_{10}?
2) Which property of a hydrocarbon determines where it condenses in a fractionating column during fractional distillation?
3) Where is crude oil found?
4) What is the general formula for alkanes?
5) How many hydrogen atoms are present in a 3-carbon alkane?
6) True or false? A molecule with the formula C_2H_4 is an alkane.
7) Give two properties of alkanes that depend on the hydrocarbon chain length.
8) How are long-chain hydrocarbons vaporised before cracking?
9) What is meant by the term 'cracking'?
10) What type of reaction is the complete combustion of a hydrocarbon?

Total:

Purity, Formulations and Gas Tests

Purity

	Everyday Definition	Chemical Definition
PURE SUBSTANCE	A substance with [____] to it, e.g. [____].	A substance containing [____] element or [____].

A chemically pure substance will:

Melt at a .... [____] at a ....
....

You can .... the purity of a sample by comparing its
.... with that of ....
....

Impurities in a sample will:
- [____] the melting point and [____] the melting range.
- [____] the boiling point and [____] the boiling range.

Formulations

FORMULATIONS — [____] mixtures with a [____].

Each component in a [____] is present in a [____] quantity, and [____] to the [____] of the formulation.

....

cleaning products

....

....

....

cosmetics

paints

....

Four Tests for Gases

① HYDROGEN burns [____] with a [____].

⚡POP! — Lighted
H_2 gas in [____]

② OXYGEN will [____] a glowing splint.

Glowing splint [____]

③ CHLORINE [____] litmus paper white.

[____]

Litmus paper

④ CARBON DIOXIDE makes limewater turn [____] when shaken with or [____] it.

[____]

Limewater — [____]

Second Go:
...... /...... /......

Purity, Formulations and Gas Tests

Purity

	Everyday Definition	Chemical Definition
PURE SUBSTANCE		

A chemically pure substance will:

Impurities in a sample will:

You can .... by
.... comparing ....
....
....

Formulations

FORMULATIONS —

Each component in

....
....
....
....
....
....
....
....

Four Tests for Gases

1 **HYDROGEN**

POP!

2 **OXYGEN**

3 **CHLORINE**

4 **CARBON DIOXIDE**

Limewater —

Topic C8 — Chemical Analysis

Paper Chromatography

Two Phases of Chromatography

CHROMATOGRAPHY — [................................] used to [................................]
the substances in a [................]. It can be used to [..].

1 STATIONARY PHASE — where the molecules [................].

e.g. [........................] paper

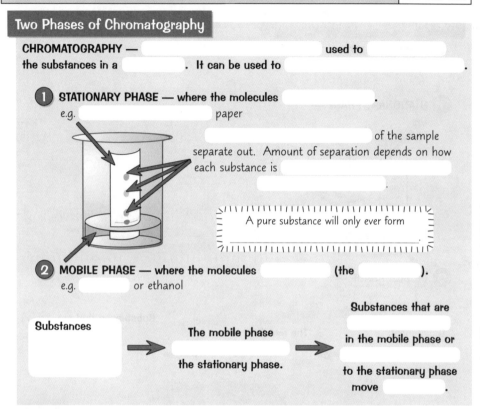

[..] of the sample
separate out. Amount of separation depends on how
each substance is [..]

[................................]

A pure substance will only ever form
..

2 MOBILE PHASE — where the molecules [................] (the [................]).

e.g. [................] or ethanol

Substances [................]
→ [................................]
the stationary phase.

The mobile phase

Substances that are
[................]
in the mobile phase or
[................]
to the stationary phase
move [................].

R$_f$ Values

R$_f$ VALUE — the [................] between the distance travelled by the
[................................] and the distance travelled by the [................].

$$R_f = \frac{\text{distance travelled by [........]} \quad (B)}{\text{distance travelled by [........]} \quad (A)}$$

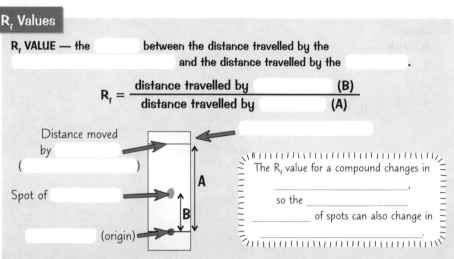

Distance moved
by [........................]
([........................])

Spot of [........................]

[................] (origin)

[................................]

A

B

The R$_f$ value for a compound changes in
..,
so the ....
.... of spots can also change in
..

 ☑ ☑ ☑

Topic C8 — Chemical Analysis

172

Paper Chromatography

Two Phases of Chromatography

CHROMATOGRAPHY —

1 STATIONARY PHASE —

e.g.

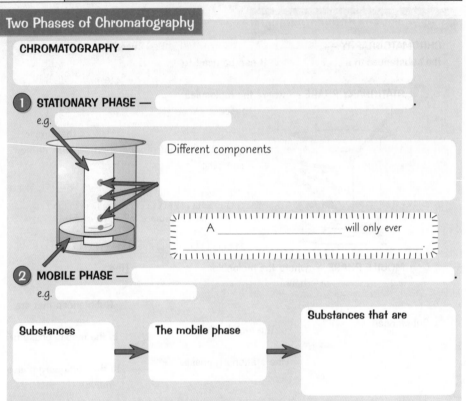

Different components

A _____ will only ever
_____.

2 MOBILE PHASE —

e.g.

Substances

The mobile phase

Substances that are

R$_f$ Values

R$_f$ VALUE —

$R_f =$

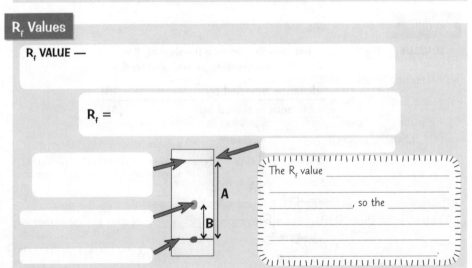

A

B

The R$_f$ value _____
_____
_____, so the _____
_____
_____.

Mixed Practice Quizzes

That's a fair few definitions and facts to remember. Luckily for you, there's a handy set of quizzes here to test what you've learned from p.169-172.

Quiz 1 Date: ...... / ...... / ......

1) Name the phase in chromatography where the molecules can't move.
2) What effect do impurities have on the boiling point of a substance?
3) Which gas will relight a glowing splint?
4) Give three examples of common formulations.
5) Which two factors determine how far a substance moves during chromatography?
6) What effect does chlorine gas have on damp litmus paper?
7) What is the chemical definition of a pure substance?
8) Which gas burns quickly with a pop when a small sample is ignited?
9) What is the definition of an R_f value?
10) Which measurements are needed for calculating an R_f value?

Total:

Quiz 2 Date: ...... / ...... / ......

1) Describe how to test for carbon dioxide.
2) What name is given to an aqueous solution of calcium hydroxide?
3) Name a substance that can be used as the mobile phase in chromatography.
4) What is chromatography?
5) Describe a test for hydrogen gas.
6) Give two effects of impurities on the melting point of a sample.
7) Why might a compound's R_f value vary between chromatograms?
8) In chromatography, what does the amount of separation of the different components in a sample depend on?
9) What determines the properties of a formulation?
10) True or false? An impure substance will always separate into the same number of spots during chromatography.

Total:

Topic C8 — Chemical Analysis

Mixed Practice Quizzes

Quiz 3 Date: ...... / ...... / ......

1) How many spots are formed by a pure substance during chromatography? ☑
2) True or false? A chemically pure substance melts at a specific temperature. ☑
3) Give an equation for the R_f value of a substance in a particular solvent. ☑
4) What is commonly used as the stationary phase in chromatography? ☑
5) True or false? In chromatography, substances that are less soluble
   in the mobile phase travel further through the stationary phase. ☑
6) How can a lighted splint be used to identify hydrogen gas? ☑
7) True or false? In chromatography, the mobile phase moves through
   the stationary phase. ☑
8) Are metal alloys an example of a formulation? ☑
9) Give two properties of a substance that can be used to determine its purity. ☑
10) Describe a test used to identify chlorine gas. ☑

Total: ____

Quiz 4 Date: ...... / ...... / ......

1) How is the chemical definition of a pure substance different from
   the definition used in everyday language? ☑
2) True or false? Medicines are chemical formulations. ☑
3) Explain how a substance separates out during chromatography. ☑
4) Describe a test for oxygen gas. ☑
5) Describe the observation that indicates a positive result
   when using limewater to test for carbon dioxide. ☑
6) True or false? Impurities in a sample cause the melting point to increase. ☑
7) What is limewater? ☑
8) Do compounds have the same R_f value in every solvent? ☑
9) What is meant by the term 'formulation'? ☑
10) True or false? Pure substances will only ever form one spot
   on a chromatogram. ☑

Total: ____

The Evolution of the Atmosphere

Volcanic Gases

Intense _____

_____

released gases.

_____ built up over time.

The early atmosphere probably contained mainly _____ and virtually _____ .

Theories about Earth's early atmosphere have _____ . They're hard to prove as it's hard to gather evidence from _____

The early atmosphere was probably like those of Mars _____ today.

Absorption of Carbon Dioxide from Atmosphere

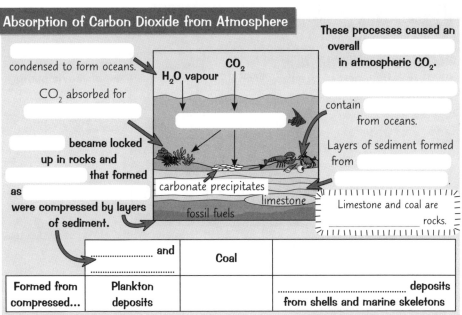

_____ condensed to form oceans.

CO_2 absorbed for _____

_____ became locked up in rocks and _____ that formed as _____ were compressed by layers of sediment.

carbonate precipitates

limestone

fossil fuels

These processes caused an overall _____ in atmospheric CO_2.

_____ contain _____ from oceans.

Layers of sediment formed from _____

Limestone and coal are _____ rocks.

Formed from compressed...	Plankton deposits	Coal	.... deposits from shells and marine skeletons
	.... and		

Increase in Oxygen

Algae evolved _____

Plants evolved over _____

These organisms produce _____ by photosynthesis.

$$6CO_2 \; + \; 6H_2O \xrightarrow{\text{light}} C_6H_{12}O_6 \; + \; \underline{}$$

water   light   oxygen

The increase in _____ led to the evolution of _____ .

Today

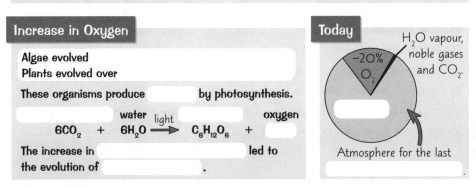

~20% O_2

H_2O vapour, noble gases and CO_2.

_____

Atmosphere for the last _____

 ☑   ☑   ☑

The Evolution of the Atmosphere

Volcanic Gases

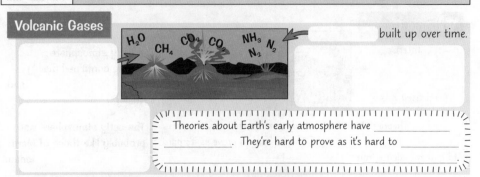

H_2O CH_4 CO_2 CO_2 NH_3 N_2 N_2

built up over time.

Theories about Earth's early atmosphere have _____ . They're hard to prove as it's hard to _____

Absorption of Carbon Dioxide from Atmosphere

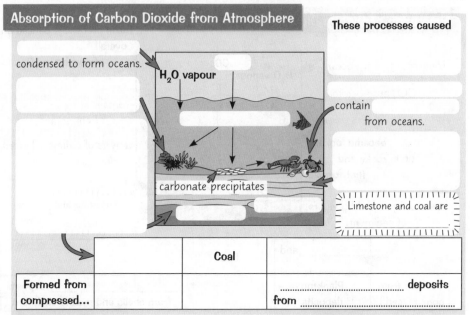

These processes caused

condensed to form oceans.

H_2O vapour

contain _____ from oceans.

carbonate precipitates

Limestone and coal are _____

	Coal	
Formed from compressed...		_____ deposits from _____

Increase in Oxygen

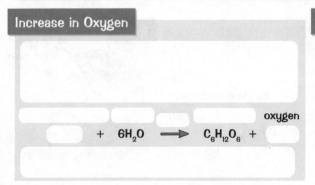

_____ + $6H_2O$ ⟶ $C_6H_{12}O_6$ + oxygen

Today

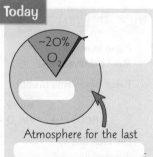

~20% O_2

Atmosphere for the last _____ .

Topic C9 — Chemistry of the Atmosphere

Greenhouse Gases & Climate Change

The Greenhouse Effect

Greenhouse Gases		
carbon dioxide		

GREENHOUSE EFFECT — when greenhouse gases in the [ ] absorb [ ] and re-radiate it in all directions, including back towards Earth, helping to keep the [ ].

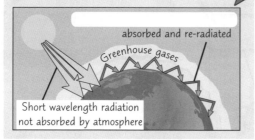

absorbed and re-radiated

Greenhouse gases

Short wavelength radiation not absorbed by atmosphere

Human Activities

Deforestation means less [ ] is removed by [ ].

[ ] fossil fuels releases [ ].

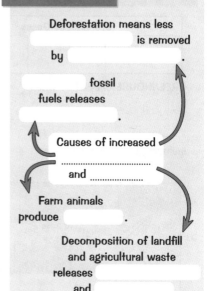

Causes of increased .... and ....

Farm animals produce [ ].

Decomposition of landfill and agricultural waste releases [ ] and [ ].

Climate Change Evidence

[ ] → Most scientists → think that → increased [ ] → have caused → the average temperature of [ ] → and this will lead to → climate change

[ ] is very complex and hard to model. This leads to oversimplified [ ] in the media where stories are biased or [ ].

Four Possible Consequences of Climate Change

1 Flooding and erosion in [ ] due to the melting of the [ ] causing sea levels to rise.

2 More frequent and severe [ ].

3 [ ] in certain areas if temperature and [ ].

4 Changes in the [ ] of some wild species if [ ].

Second Go:
...... /...... /......

Greenhouse Gases & Climate Change

The Greenhouse Effect

Greenhouse Gases		

GREENHOUSE EFFECT — when

including back towards Earth,

.

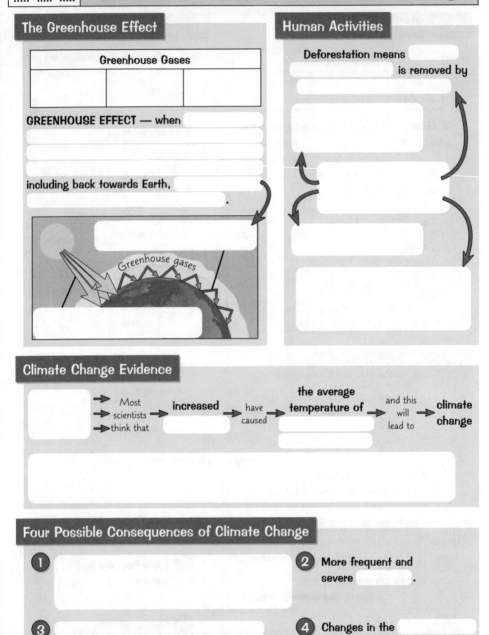

Greenhouse gases

Human Activities

Deforestation means

is removed by

Climate Change Evidence

Most scientists think that → increased → have caused → the average temperature of → and this will lead to → climate change

Four Possible Consequences of Climate Change

1

2 More frequent and severe

3

in certain areas if temperature and

.

4 Changes in the

of some wild species if

.

Topic C9 — Chemistry of the Atmosphere

Carbon Footprints and Air Pollution

Carbon Footprints

CARBON FOOTPRINT — how much _____ and other greenhouse gases are released over _____
— e.g. _____ .

- _____ emissions reduces the carbon footprint.

- Actions to _____ may be limited _____ are unwilling or unable to make _____ .

Air Pollution

Fossil fuels contain _____ and sometimes _____ .

_____ releases _____ which pollute the air.

doesn't have any colour or smell, so it's hard to _____ .

Pollutant	Formation	Effects
....	carbon particulates .... water vapour	Stops blood from transporting .... around the body — this can cause ....' .... or ....
carbon particulates (............)	.... of fossil fuels (e.g. coal).	.... problems Global ....
sulfur dioxide	.... of .... in fossil fuels during combustion.	NO$_x$ SO$_2$ damage to ...., statues and .... problems
oxides of	Reaction between .... and .... in the air caused by the ....' e.g. in car engines.	

Carbon Footprints and Air Pollution

Carbon Footprints

CARBON FOOTPRINT —

- Reducing

-

Air Pollution

Fossil fuels contain _____ and sometimes _____ .

_____ doesn't have _____ , so it's hard to _____ .

Pollutant	....	Effects
	.... water vapour .... of fossil fuels (e.g. coal).	Stops .... around the body — this can cause ....,' .... or ....
	Reaction between .... and .... in the air caused by the	NO$_x$ SO$_2$ ....

Mixed Practice Quizzes

A lot to learn there, but p.175-180 will help you understand how Earth's atmosphere has changed over billions of years, as well as helping you to answer these quizzes.

Quiz 1   Date: ...... / ...... / ......

1) Give one human activity that contributes to increased levels of methane in the atmosphere.

2) What are crude oil and natural gas formed from?

3) Roughly what percentage of the atmosphere today is nitrogen?

4) Which pollutants can react with water in clouds to form acid rain?

5) What is the definition of a carbon footprint?

6) Why is it hard to find evidence about what Earth's early atmosphere was like?

7) Give the balanced symbol equation for photosynthesis.

8) How did the oceans form from the early atmosphere?

9) True or false? The Earth's atmosphere absorbs more long wavelength radiation than short wavelength radiation.

10) Why is it difficult to detect carbon monoxide?

Total: ☐

Quiz 2   Date: ...... / ...... / ......

1) Give two of the problems caused by carbon particulates in the air.

2) Name three greenhouse gases.

3) How do scientists think that gases were released into the early atmosphere?

4) What are the two products of photosynthesis?

5) How did the formation of oceans lead to a decrease in the amount of carbon dioxide in the atmosphere?

6) Describe one possible negative effect of climate change.

7) Roughly how many years ago did algae evolve?

8) How is sulfur dioxide produced from fossil fuels?

9) What type of rock are coal and limestone?

10) What change in the Earth's early atmosphere enabled animals to evolve?

Total: ☐

Mixed Practice Quizzes

Quiz 3   Date: ...... / ...... / ......

1) Which fossil fuel is formed from compressed plant deposits?
2) How do greenhouse gases in the atmosphere keep the Earth warm?
3) Most scientists believe that increased levels of carbon dioxide will lead to climate change. What is this belief based on?
4) How can a carbon footprint be reduced?
5) How is nitrogen thought to have built up in Earth's early atmosphere?
6) Give one problem associated with increased carbon monoxide in the air.
7) Roughly what percentage of Earth's atmosphere today is oxygen?
8) True or false? Fossil fuel formation resulted in an increase in atmospheric carbon dioxide.
9) Which atmospheric gas is absorbed by plants and algae for photosynthesis?
10) What were the layers of sediment on the seabed formed from?

Total:

Quiz 4   Date: ...... / ...... / ......

1) Give two problems caused by sulfur dioxide pollution.
2) How can burning fuel lead to the production of oxides of nitrogen?
3) Which two planets have atmospheres thought to be similar to that of the early Earth?
4) Name one gas that makes up a small proportion of Earth's current atmosphere today.
5) How were limestone deposits formed?
6) True or false? One theory suggests that the Earth's early atmosphere contained mainly carbon dioxide.
7) Name two pollutants produced by the incomplete combustion of a fuel.
8) Give one problem caused by acid rain.
9) Give one reason why media stories on climate change are often biased or missing information.
10) Name one element which is often found as an impurity in fossil fuels.

Total:

Topic C9 — Chemistry of the Atmosphere

Resources & Life Cycle Assessments

First Go:
..... / ..... / .....

Resources

Humans use [＿＿＿＿＿＿＿＿] for a variety of different purposes:

[＿＿＿＿] Clothing Shelter Fuel for transport [＿＿＿＿]

We can use [＿＿＿＿＿＿＿＿] products in place of certain natural resources, e.g. rubber can be replaced by [＿＿＿＿＿＿＿] .

Some natural resources are FINITE — [＿＿＿＿＿＿＿＿＿＿] .

Nuclear fuel [＿＿＿＿] Coal

RENEWABLE RESOURCES — resources that reform at a [＿＿＿＿＿＿＿＿] , e.g. timber.

[＿＿＿＿] are processed to provide materials and energy.

Life Cycle Assessments

LIFE CYCLE ASSESSMENT (LCA) — an assessment of the [＿＿＿＿＿＿] [＿＿＿＿] of a product over each stage of its life.

Life Cycle Assessment Stage	Plastic Bag	Paper Bag
		Timber
Manufacturing and Packaging	Key compounds extracted by .... Waste has other uses.	Takes a lot of energy to pulp timber and creates lots of waste
	Reusable	
Product	Recyclable, ...	.... and recyclable

- Some factors [＿＿＿＿＿＿＿＿] are easily quantified.
- Some factors [＿＿＿＿＿＿＿＿＿＿] are hard to measure or depend on a person's opinion. This can make life cycle assessments biased.
- SELECTIVE LCA — LCA where [＿＿＿＿＿＿＿＿] has been removed to make [＿＿＿＿＿＿＿] than it really is, [＿＿＿＿＿＿＿＿] .

Second Go: ..... / ..... /	# Resources & Life Cycle Assessments

Resources

Humans use _____ :

	Clothing	Shelter	Fuel for	

We can use _____ in place of certain

_____ , e.g. _____ can be replaced by _____ .

Some natural resources are **FINITE** — _____ .

_____ _____ _____

fuel

RENEWABLE RESOURCES — _____

_____ are processed to provide

Life Cycle Assessments

LIFE CYCLE ASSESSMENT (LCA) — _____

Life Cycle Assessment Stage	Plastic Bag	Paper Bag
Raw Materials		
	Reusable	
Product Disposal		

- Some factors _____

- Some factors _____ are hard to measure or depend on a person's opinion. This can make _____ .

- **SELECTIVE LCA** — _____

Reuse and Recycling

Improving Sustainability

SUSTAINABLE DEVELOPMENT — meeting the needs of present society while not damaging the lives of _____.

Three ways to improve sustainability:

1 _____ the amount of raw materials used

2 Reusing products instead of _____

3 _____ products that can't be _____

_____ reduces the amount of _____ we need to extract, as well as the _____ involved in their extraction.

> Mining for raw materials is bad for the _____.

Recycling Metals

Recycling metals helps to save on the _____ required to mine and _____.

_____

↓

Melted down

↓

_____ into new products

Amount of _____ required for recyclable metals depends on the _____ and _____.

> Both _____ and _____ can be added to iron in a _____ together to reduce the amount of _____ required.

Recycling Glass

Waste glass

↓

Separated by colour and _____

↓

_____

↓

Reshaped

> Glass bottles can also be _____ instead of recycling them.

 ☑ ☑ ☑

Topic C10 — Using Resources

Reuse and Recycling

Improving Sustainability

_____ — meeting the needs of present society
_____ .

Three ways to improve sustainability:

> Mining for raw materials is bad
> for the _____ .

1 Reducing _____

2 Reusing _____

3 _____ products that can't be _____

_____ reduces
the amount of _____ .
as well as the _____ .

Recycling Metals

Recycling metals

_____

↓

Melted down

↓

_____

Amount of _____ required for
recyclable metals depends on
the _____ .

> Both _____ and _____
> can be added to _____
> _____
> _____
> _____ .

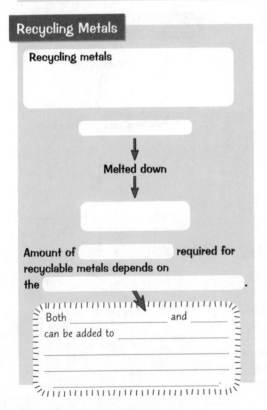

Recycling Glass

Waste glass

↓

_____

↓

_____

↓

_____

> Glass bottles can also
> be _____ instead
> of recycling them.

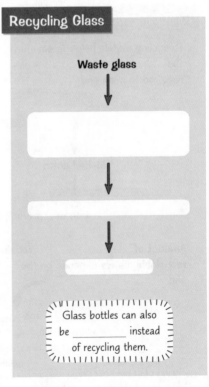

Treating Water

Potable Water

POTABLE WATER — _____ .

Type of Water	Source	Treatment
Ground water	Underground rocks	Must be .... and sterilised
Salt water	Sea water	Must be ....
	Sewage treatment and agricultural systems	Requires a lot of treatment

Potable water is not .... It can contain low levels of .... and ....

Treating Ground Water

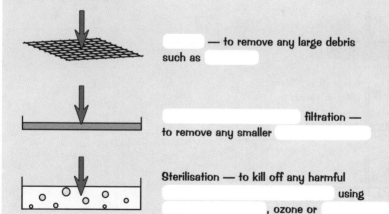

_____ — to remove any large debris such as _____

_____ filtration — to remove any smaller _____

Sterilisation — to kill off any harmful _____ using _____ , ozone or _____

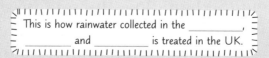

This is how rainwater collected in the _____ , _____ and _____ is treated in the UK.

Treating Water

Potable Water

POTABLE WATER — _____ .

Type of Water	Source	
Ground water		
Salt water		

Potable water is _____ . It can contain low levels of _____ and _____ .

Treating Ground Water

_____ — to remove _____

_____

Sterilisation — _____

This is how rainwater collected in the _____, _____ and _____ is treated in the UK.

Topic C10 — Using Resources

Desalination & Treating Waste Water

Two Methods of Desalination

Desalination is carried out in [   ]
[   ] to make sea water [   ].

1 DISTILLATION — [   ] the water to
separate it from [   ].

2 [   ] — passing the water through a [   ]
that only allows [   ] through.

These methods use ....

Treating Waste Water

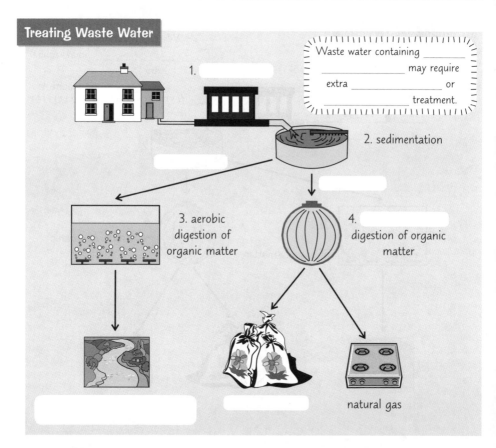

1. [   ]

Waste water containing ....
.... may require
extra .... or
.... treatment.

2. sedimentation

3. aerobic digestion of organic matter

4. [   ] digestion of organic matter

natural gas

Second Go:
...../...../.....

Desalination & Treating Waste Water

Two Methods of Desalination

Desalination

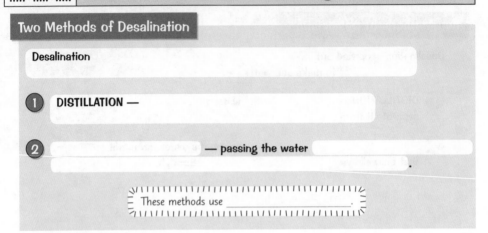

1. **DISTILLATION —**

2. _____ — passing the water _____ .

These methods use _____ .

Treating Waste Water

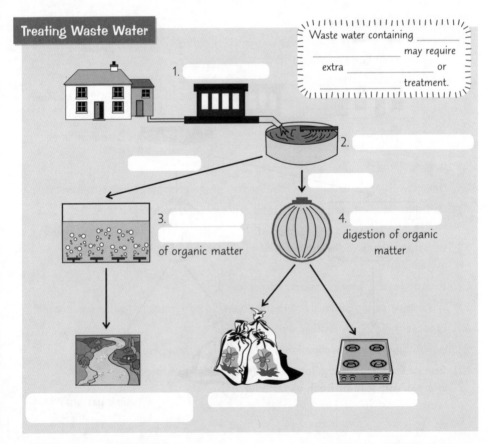

Waste water containing _____ _____ may require extra _____ or _____ treatment.

1. _____

2. _____

3. _____ of organic matter

4. _____ digestion of organic matter

 ✓ ✓ ✓

Mixed Practice Quizzes

Congratulations, you've made it all the way to the end of Topic C10.
Now collect your prize — four perfectly constructed quizzes all about p.183-190.

Quiz 1   Date: ...... / ...... / ......

1) What is meant by a 'renewable resource'?
2) How are small solids removed from ground water?
3) What is meant by 'potable water'?
4) State a benefit of recycling metals.
5) Give one example of a finite resource.
6) What is carried out to identify the environmental impact of a new product?
7) Give two types of product that can be used in place of natural resources.
8) What steps can be taken to treat waste water containing toxic substances?
9) What happens to the effluent from the treatment of waste water before it is released to the environment?
10) Give a problem associated with desalinating water.

Total:

Quiz 2   Date: ...... / ...... / ......

1) What are the steps involved in recycling glass?
2) Is potable water chemically pure?
3) Describe the purpose of the sterilisation stage of ground water treatment.
4) Is it easiest to obtain potable water from ground water, waste water or salt water?
5) What two things does the amount of separation required for recycling metals depend on?
6) True or false? Metals cannot be recycled.
7) What type of digestion does the sludge undergo in waste water treatment?
8) What is a life cycle assessment (LCA)?
9) Which method of desalination involves boiling the water?
10) True or false? Desalination of water is typically carried out in areas with lots of fresh water sources.

Total:

Mixed Practice Quizzes

Quiz 3   Date: ...... / ...... / ......

1) What is meant by a selective LCA?
2) What are the two products of the sedimentation of waste water?
3) Give an example of a natural resource that can be replaced by a man-made product.
4) What is the source of the fresh water that collects in the ground and lakes and rivers?
5) What might processed finite resources be used for?
6) Give a reason why desalination might be used to produce potable water.
7) Which product comes from a finite resource: plastic bags or paper bags?
8) Describe what happens in the reverse osmosis of sea water.
9) Which type of resource reforms at a faster rate than it is used up?
10) Give two examples of things present in small quantities in potable water.

Total:

Quiz 4   Date: ...... / ...... / ......

1) Compare the treatment of ground water and waste water to produce potable water.
2) State three purposes which humans use natural resources for.
3) What can be used to kill off harmful microbes during the sterilisation stage of ground water treatment?
4) What is the purpose of sustainable development?
5) What is the first stage of waste water treatment?
6) Why might two LCAs on the same product be different?
7) Give the four stages of a product's life that are considered in a life cycle assessment.
8) Give two products that can be made from sludge in waste water treatment.
9) How can glass bottles be used sustainably without recycling them?
10) True or false? In the UK, potable water is mainly obtained by desalination of salt water.

Total:

Energy Stores, Transfers and Systems

First Go:
..... /..... /.....

Eight Types of Energy Store

1. [____]
2. [____] potential
3. [____] potential
4. Electrostatic
5. [____]
6. Chemical
7. Magnetic
8. [____]

Four Types of Energy Transfer

1. [____] (a force doing work)
2. Electrical ([____])
3. [____]
4. Radiation (e.g. [____])

[____] = energy transferred.

Energy Transfers in Five Different Systems

SYSTEM — a single object or ....

1 Arm throwing ball up

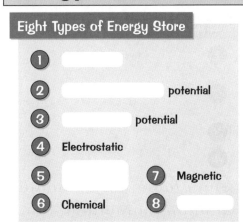

[____]
store of arm.

force exerted ____
____ does ____

Kinetic energy store [____].

2 Ball falling

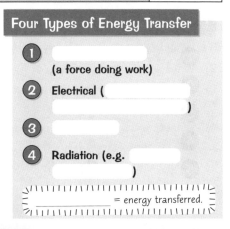

Gravitational potential energy
[____].

____ does work

[____]
of ball.

3 Brakes applied to car wheels

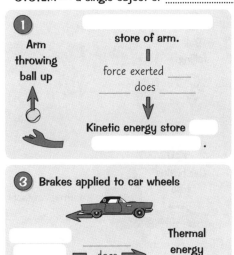

[____]
stores of wheels.
— does work →
Thermal energy
[____].

4 Car hitting tree

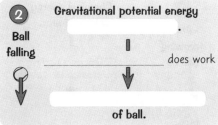

Kinetic energy [____].

normal contact force ____

[____]
— e.g. elastic potential energy stores [____].

5 Kettle's heating element and water

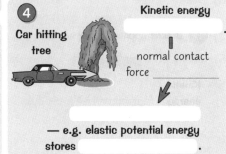

[____] energy ____ →
[____]
store of kettle's [____] element.
— energy transferred ____ →
[____]
store of water.

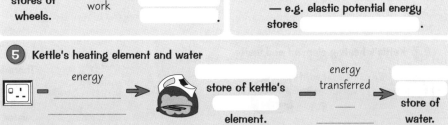
 ☑   ☑   ☑

Second Go:
..... / ..... / .....

Energy Stores, Transfers and Systems

Eight Types of Energy Store

1
2
3
4
5   7
6   8

Four Types of Energy Transfer

1
2
3
4

_____ = _____

Energy Transfers in Five Different Systems

SYSTEM — ....

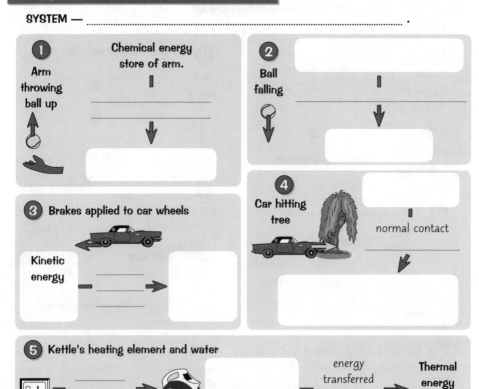

1 Arm throwing ball up

Chemical energy store of arm.

2 Ball falling

3 Brakes applied to car wheels

Kinetic energy

4 Car hitting tree

normal contact

5 Kettle's heating element and water

energy transferred

Thermal energy store of water.

Topic P1 — Energy

Energy, Power and Efficiency

Kinetic Energy

Kinetic energy ( )

$$E_k = \tfrac{1}{2}m\quad^2$$

(kg)   speed ( )

Gravitational Potential Energy

(kg)

(J) $E_p = mgh$ (m)

gravitational _____ ( )

Conservation of Energy and Specific Heat Capacity

CONSERVATION OF ENERGY — energy can be _____.

_____ or _____ but not _____ or _____.

Energy _____
(by heating) _____

_____, increasing its _____

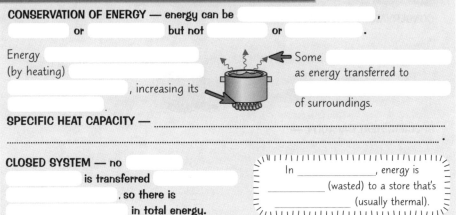

Some _____
as energy transferred to

_____
of surroundings.

SPECIFIC HEAT CAPACITY — ....

....

CLOSED SYSTEM — no _____
is transferred _____
_____, so there is
_____ in total energy.

In _____, energy is
_____ (wasted) to a store that's
_____ (usually thermal).

Power

POWER — _____
(or rate of doing work).
One watt (W) = one _____ of energy
_____.

energy transferred ( )

(J)

$$P = \frac{E}{t}$$

power ( )   _____ (s)

$$P = \frac{}{t}$$

power ( )   _____ (s)

2 W motor transfers

_____ than 1 W
motor, so lifts mass faster.

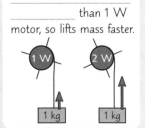

1 W   2 W

1 kg   1 kg

Efficiency Equations

Efficiency = $\dfrac{\text{_____ energy transfer}}{\text{Total input _____}}$

Efficiency = $\dfrac{}{\text{Total power input}}$

No device is _____.

Multiply by _____
to get _____.

Energy, Power and Efficiency

Kinetic Energy

$$E_k = \tfrac{1}{2}mv^2$$

Gravitational Potential Energy

height (m)

$$E_p = $$

Conservation of Energy and Specific Heat Capacity

CONSERVATION OF ENERGY —

Energy

Some energy dissipated

SPECIFIC HEAT CAPACITY —

CLOSED SYSTEM —

In _____, energy is
_____ to a store that's
_____ .

Power

POWER —

One watt (W) =

$$P = \frac{\quad}{\text{time (s)}}$$

$$P = \frac{\quad}{\text{time (s)}}$$

_____ than 1 W
motor _____
_____ .

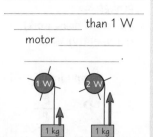

Efficiency Equations

Efficiency = ──────────────

Efficiency = ──────────────

Multiply by _____ .

Reducing Unwanted Energy Transfers

Conduction

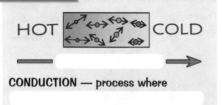

HOT ▨ COLD

CONDUCTION — process where

[_____]

to neighbouring particles.

Convection

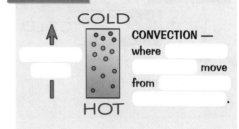

COLD

CONVECTION — where [_____] move from [_____].

HOT

Lubrication and Thermal Insulation

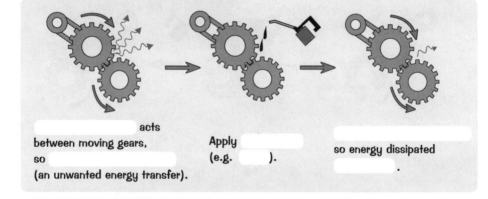

[_____] acts between moving gears, so [_____] (an unwanted energy transfer).

Apply [_____] (e.g. [____]).

[_____] so energy dissipated [_____].

Thermal insulation (e.g. [_____]) reduces unwanted energy transfers [_____].

Two Ways to Decrease How Quickly a Building Cools

1 Increase [____] of its [____].

2 Make walls out of material with [_____].

The higher a material's

....,'
the .... it transfers
energy by ....

Topic P1 — Energy

Reducing Unwanted Energy Transfers

Conduction

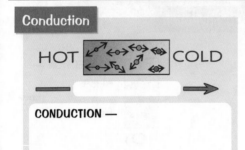

HOT COLD

CONDUCTION —

Convection

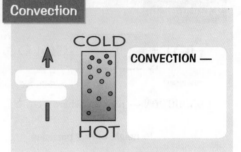

COLD

HOT

CONVECTION —

Lubrication and Thermal Insulation

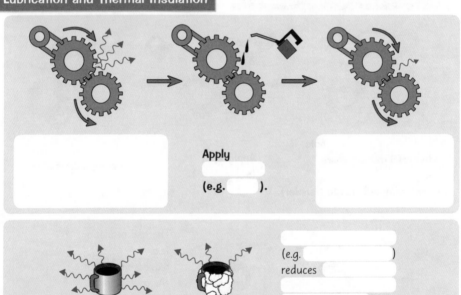

Apply

(e.g.).

(e.g.)
reduces

Two Ways to Decrease How Quickly a Building Cools

1. The higher

2. Make walls

Topic P1 — Energy

Non-Renewables and Renewables

Non-Renewable and Renewable Energy Resources

NON-RENEWABLE ENERGY RESOURCES — energy resources that will _____ .

All energy resources used to ....

RENEWABLE ENERGY RESOURCES — energy resources that will _____ .

Some energy resources used for ....

Three Fossil Fuels | Non-renewable |

1 Coal

Burned for _____ and used to power _____ .

2 Oil

Used to make _____ (_____) for cars.

3 (Natural) Gas

Used to _____ that is then _____ .

Fossil fuels are _____ .

- Burning fossil fuels _____ , contributing to _____ .
- Burning coal and oil releases _____ , causing _____ .

| Reliable |

Nuclear Power | _____ |

Nuclear fuel _____ in nuclear _____ , _____ .

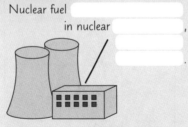

- Nuclear waste is _____ _____ to _____ .
- Carries the risk of a _____ .

_____

Wind Power | Renewable |

Wind turns _____ , generating _____ .

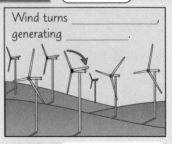

- Produce _____ when in use.
- _____
- _____

Unreliable — Turbines stop turning when ....

Non-Renewables and Renewables

Non-Renewable and Renewable Energy Resources

NON-RENEWABLE ENERGY
RESOURCES —

.... used
to ....

RENEWABLE ENERGY RESOURCES —

.... used
for ....

Three Fossil Fuels

1 Coal

and
used to

2

Used to

3

Used to

Fossil fuels are

* **Burning**
* **Burning**

Nuclear Power

Nuclear

* **Nuclear waste**

* **Carries the risk**

Wind Power

Wind

*
*
*

Unreliable — ....
....

Renewables

Solar Power

Solar cells

....
directly from
....

• **Produce** [   ]
  when in use.

Reliable (..........................)
....

.... use the
sun to .... which is
then pumped into ....

Geothermal Power

power plant

water

hot rock

Energy from ....
.... of
underground hot rocks
used to ....
....

• **Do very little** [   ]
  [   ] .

[   ] ....
.... are used to

Hydro-electric Power [Renewable]

..................., built in
valley, ...

Water allowed out ....
..............................., generating electricity.

• **Produce** [   ]
  when in use.

• [   ] (from
  flooding the valley) release
  [   ] ,
  contributing to global warming.

Reliable (except ....
...............................).

Wave Power [Renewable]

air

Waves move [   ] → Air forced [   ] → [   ]

• **Produce** [   ] when in use.
• **Disturb habitats of**
  [   ] .

[   ]

Unreliable — ....
....

Renewables

Solar Power

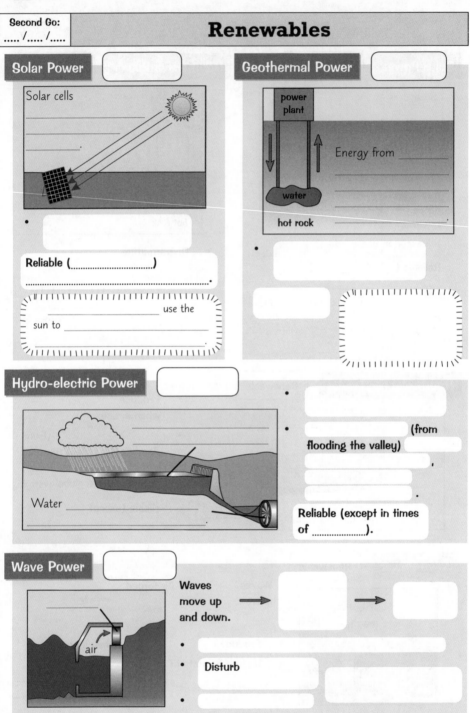

Solar cells

_____
....
_____ .

• _____

Reliable (........................)
....

_____ use the
sun to _____
_____ .

Geothermal Power

power plant

Energy from _____
....
....
....

water

hot rock ....

• _____

Hydro-electric Power

Water _____
_____ .

• _____

• _____ (from
flooding the valley)
_____ ,
_____
_____ .

**Reliable (except in times
of ....).**

Wave Power

air

Waves
move up
and down. ➡ ➡

• _____

• **Disturb** _____

• _____

Topic P1 — Energy

Renewables and Trends

Tidal Barrages [Renewable]

Tide comes in.

↓

Water builds

_____ .

↓

Water _____ . → _____

- Produce _____ when in use.
- Disturb habitats of _____ .
- _____ .

Reliable — ....
....

_____ built across _____

Bio-fuels [_____]

Made from _____
or _____ .

Bio-fuels are burned to
_____ .

- In some regions,
  _____
  _____ destroyed to
  _____ ,
  so species lose
  _____ .

Reliable

Bio-fuels are also _____
_____ and used
as _____ .

Trends in Energy Use

1900 ⇒ Electricity use increased as:
– 2000
- _____ and people began to use
  _____ .

2000 ⇒ Electricity use decreasing as:
onwards
- appliances are _____ .
- people are _____ with amount of _____ .

Three reasons why we're increasing use of renewables:

1️⃣ _____ is very damaging to environment.

2️⃣ We need to _____
_____ without _____
before they run out.

3️⃣ Pressure on _____
have led them to _____
_____ .

Scientists can advise others to use _____ , but don't
have the power to _____ . Change limited by _____

204

Renewables and Trends

Tidal Barrages

Tide comes in.

Reliable — ....
....

Bio-fuels

Made from

Bio-fuels

• In some regions,

Bio-fuels are also burned for heating and ....
....

Trends in Energy Use

1900 – 2000 ⟹ Electricity use increased as:
•

2000 onwards ⟹ Electricity use decreasing as:
•
•

Three reasons why we're increasing use of renewables:

1

2   3

Scientists ....
.... Change ....
....

Topic P1 — Energy

Mixed Practice Quizzes

If you think doing quizzes based on stuff from pages 193-204 sounds like a bad idea, don't look down. Oh no, you looked. That means you have to do them now.

Quiz 1   Date: ...... / ...... / ......

1) State two environmental impacts of burning fossil fuels.

2) In what type of system is there no overall change in energy when energy is transferred?

3) Would a building cool quicker with thinner or thicker walls?

4) Give one reason why electricity use increased from 1900 to 2000.

5) Name three types of energy stores.

6) True or false? In some systems, energy is never dissipated.

7) What is one joule of energy per second in watts?

8) Give two equations that can be used to calculate power.

9) What are bio-fuels made from?

10) Describe how energy is transferred when a car hits a tree.

Total:

Quiz 2   Date: ...... / ...... / ......

1) True or false? Energy can be transferred usefully, created or destroyed.

2) Which one of the following is a non-renewable energy resource?
   A. Wind power   B. Bio-fuels   C. Tidal power   D. Nuclear power

3) Describe how energy is transferred when a kettle boils water.

4) What is meant by the specific heat capacity of a substance?

5) Which is more reliable, wave power or solar power?

6) Give two reasons why the use of renewable energy resources is increasing.

7) What equation can be used to find the amount of energy in an object's kinetic energy store?

8) Name three renewable energy resources.

9) State two negative impacts tidal barrages have on the environment.

10) True or false? Thermal insulation reduces unwanted energy stores.

Total:

Mixed Practice Quizzes

Quiz 3   Date: ...... / ...... / ......

1) True or false? The higher a material's thermal conductivity,
   the faster it transfers energy by conduction.

2) Name three types of fossil fuel. Give one use for each type of fossil fuel.

3) Describe one environmental impact of using nuclear power.

4) State one way you could reduce the frictional
   forces acting between moving gears.

5) What equation can be used to find the amount of energy
   in an object's gravitational potential energy store?

6) Scientists can advise others to change from non-renewable to renewable
   energy resources, but what factors is this change limited by?

7) What type of energy store is dissipated energy usually transferred to?

8) What is meant by a renewable energy resource?

9) True or false? Energy can be transferred magnetically.

10) Explain why tidal power is more reliable than wave power.

Total:

Quiz 4   Date: ...... / ...... / ......

1) What is meant by a system?

2) Describe one environmental impact of using hydro-electric power.

3) What is meant by the conservation of energy?

4) Give two equations that can be used to calculate efficiency.

5) Explain how using lubrication on moving gears
   can reduce the energy they dissipate.

6) State two negative impacts wind turbines have on the environment.

7) Name an energy resource that doesn't produce pollution when in use.

8) True or false? A 2 W motor would lift a 1 kg mass faster than a 1 W motor.

9) Describe the changes in the way energy is stored when:
   a) a ball is thrown upwards   b) a ball falls under gravity

10) Energy resources can be used to generate electricity.
    State two other uses of energy resources.

Total:

Current

Current, Potential Difference and Resistance

	Definition	Unit
CURRENT	flow of	........................., A
POTENTIAL DIFFERENCE	.... that pushes charge round	volt, ...
RESISTANCE	anything that .... charge flow	ohm, ...

Current in Circuits

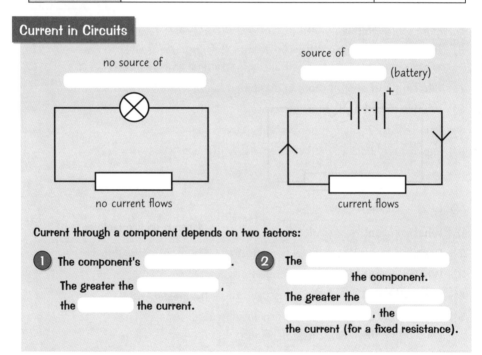

no source of
[_____]

no current flows

source of
[_____]
[_____] (battery)

current flows

Current through a component depends on two factors:

1 The component's [_____].
The greater the [_____],
the [____] the current.

2 The [_____]
[_____] the component.
The greater the [_____]
[_____], the [_____]
the current (for a fixed resistance).

Charge in Circuits

size of the current = rate of [_____]

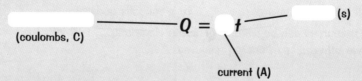

[_____] (coulombs, C) ———— $Q = \quad t$ ———— [_____] (s)

current (A)

Second Go: ...../...../.....

Current

Current, Potential Difference and Resistance

	Definition	Unit
CURRENT		
POTENTIAL DIFFERENCE		
RESISTANCE		

Current in Circuits

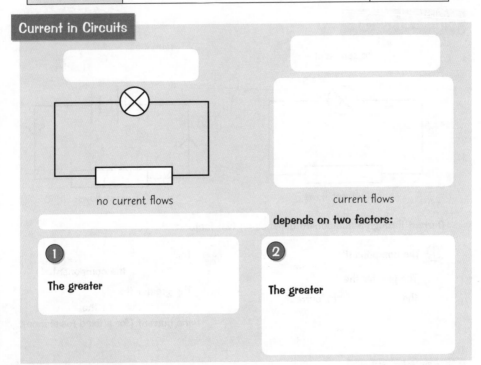

no current flows

current flows

depends on two factors:

1

The greater

2

The greater

Charge in Circuits

size of the [____] = [_____]

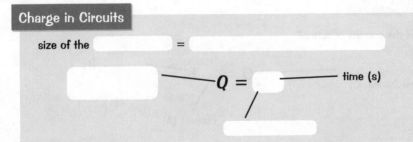

[_____] — $Q =$ [____] — time (s)

V = IR and Circuit Symbols

Potential Difference Equation

potential difference ( ) ——— ***V = IR*** ———[ ] (Ω)

[ ] (A)

Circuit Symbols

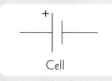

Cell

Battery

....

Voltmeter

Ammeter

Switch closed

....

Variable resistor

....

Diode

LDR (Light-Dependent Resistor)

....

LED (....)

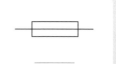

....

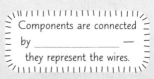
Components are connected by .... — they represent the wires.

$V = IR$ and Circuit Symbols

Potential Difference Equation

potential difference (V)

Circuit Symbols

_____	Battery	_____
_____	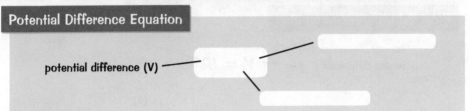 A _____	_____
_____	_____	_____
_____	LDR (Light-Dependent Resistor)	_____
LED (Light-Emitting Diode)	_____	Components are connected by

I-V Characteristics & Circuit Devices

Three Different *I-V* Characteristics

1 Ohmic conductor (e.g. a resistor) ─[▭]─ at constant temperature

Current is [   ] to potential difference...

... so resistance [   ].

This graph is ....

Components with changing resistance (when current through them varies):

[   ] [   ]

2 Filament lamp [   ]

Current increases...

... so [   ] of filament increases...

... so resistance [   ].

3 Diode [   ]

[   ] in one direction...

... so current [   ] [   ].

These graphs are ....

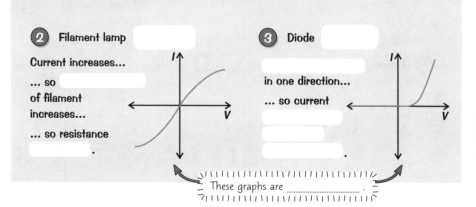

LDRs and Thermistors

	LDR [ ]	Thermistor [ ]
[ ] depends on...	light intensity	temperature
Lower resistance in...		
Used in...	automatic night lights	

 ☑   ☑   ☑

212

I-V Characteristics & Circuit Devices

Three Different *I-V* Characteristics

1 [_____] —⊏□⊐—

(e.g. a [_____]) at constant temperature

[_____]

⌁⌁⌁⌁⌁⌁⌁⌁⌁⌁⌁⌁⌁⌁⌁⌁⌁⌁⌁⌁⌁
This graph is ....
⌁⌁⌁⌁⌁⌁⌁⌁⌁⌁⌁⌁⌁⌁⌁⌁⌁⌁⌁⌁⌁

Components with [_____]

[_____] :

[_____]

2 Filament lamp [_____]

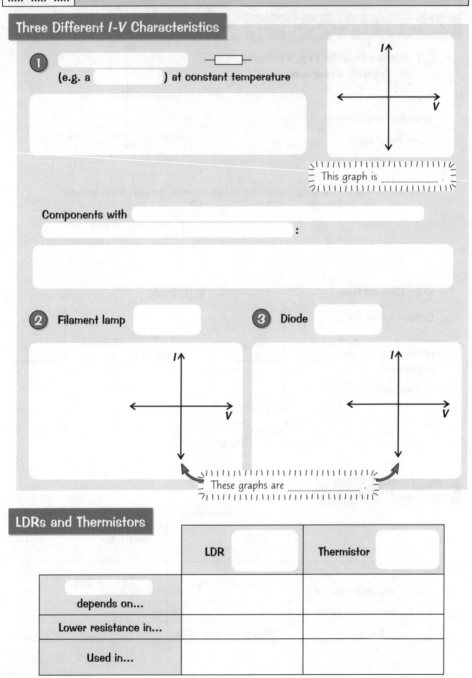

3 Diode [_____]

⌁⌁⌁⌁⌁⌁⌁⌁⌁⌁⌁⌁⌁⌁⌁⌁⌁⌁⌁⌁⌁⌁
These graphs are ....
⌁⌁⌁⌁⌁⌁⌁⌁⌁⌁⌁⌁⌁⌁⌁⌁⌁⌁⌁⌁⌁⌁

LDRs and Thermistors

	LDR [____]	Thermistor [____]
[_____] depends on...		
Lower resistance in...		
Used in...		

Topic P2 — Electricity

Mixed Practice Quizzes

Here are some quick-fire quiz questions to test what you've done on p.207-212.
No — don't mention it. Mark each test yourself and tot up your score.

Quiz 1 | Date: ...... / ...... / ......

1) True or false? The *I-V* graph of a diode is linear.
2) What does the circuit symbol '—⊗—' represent?
3) What electrical property is measured in amperes?
4) True or false? Potential difference is measured in volts.
5) What is the circuit symbol for a diode?
6) What happens to the resistance of an LDR when light intensity increases?
7) For a component with a fixed resistance, what happens to the current through the component if the potential difference across it is increased?
8) What shape does the *I-V* graph of an ohmic conductor have?
9) What is the equation for charge flow?
10) What is the circuit symbol for an LDR?

Total:

Quiz 2 | Date: ...... / ...... / ......

1) What is the circuit symbol for an open switch?
2) Give an example of an ohmic conductor.
3) What shape does the *I-V* graph for a diode have?
4) What is the unit of current?
5) What is the equation that links potential difference, current and resistance?
6) What does the circuit symbol '—Ⓥ—' represent?
7) What does the resistance of a thermistor depend on?
8) Give one application for an LDR.
9) What must be included in a circuit in order for current to flow?
10) Explain the shape of an *I-V* graph for a filament lamp.

Total:

Mixed Practice Quizzes

Quiz 3   Date: ...... / ...... / ......

1) What does the circuit symbol '—○—○—' represent?
2) Give one application for a thermistor.
3) What property is measured in coulombs?
4) What are the units of resistance?
5) What will happen to the current through a component if its resistance increases while the potential difference across it stays the same?
6) What is the circuit symbol for a battery?
7) True or false? An ohmic conductor at a constant temperature has a constant resistance.
8) Why does no current flow in a circuit which only contains a filament lamp and a resistor connected in a closed loop?
9) Explain the shape of an *I-V* graph for a diode.
10) What is the circuit symbol for a fuse?

Total:

Quiz 4   Date: ...... / ...... / ......

1) What is the circuit symbol for a thermistor?
2) What is electric current?
3) What electrical device has an *I-V* graph that is a straight line through the origin?
4) Name two circuit devices whose resistance changes when the current through them changes.
5) Name the device whose resistance decreases as the light on it gets brighter.
6) True or false? The size of a current is equal to the rate of flow of charge.
7) State the two factors that the current through a component depends on.
8) What does the circuit symbol '—◁—' represent?
9) True or false? The *I-V* graph of a filament lamp is a straight line through the origin.
10) What is the circuit symbol for a variable resistor?

Total:

Series and Parallel Circuits

Series Circuits

Current is [_____].

$$I_1 = \boxed{}$$

Total source potential difference is [_____].

$$V_{total} = \boxed{}$$

Total resistance of components
= [_____].

$$R_{total} = \boxed{}$$

Adding a resistor in series [_____] the total resistance of the circuit.

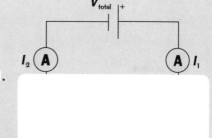

Parallel Circuits

Total current flowing around a
circuit = [_____]
[_____].

$$I_{total} = \boxed{}$$

Potential difference across each
branch is the same as [_____]
[_____].

$$V_1 = V_2 = \boxed{}$$

The total resistance of resistors
in parallel is [_____] the
resistance of the smallest resistor.

Adding a resistor in parallel [_____] the total resistance of the circuit.

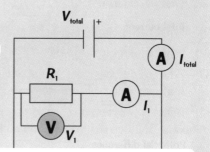

Series and Parallel Circuits

Series Circuits

Current

☐ = ☐

Total source

☐ = ☐

Total resistance

☐ = ☐

Adding a resistor in series

Parallel Circuits

Total current

☐ = ☐

Potential difference

☐ = ☐ = ☐

The total resistance of resistors in parallel

Adding a resistor in parallel

 ✓ ✓ ☺ ✓

Electricity in the Home

Two Types of Electricity Supply

1 [_____] — current that constantly changes direction and is produced by [_____]. Used in mains supply.

2 [_____] — current that always flows in the same direction and is produced by [_____]. Supplied by batteries.

Three Facts about UK Mains

1 [_____] supply

2 frequency of [_____]

3 voltage around [_____]

Three-core Cables

* Most [_____] have a three-core cable.
* The insulation on each wire has a particular [_____] to identify it.

(green and yellow)

(blue)

(brown)

	live wire	neutral wire	earth wire
Colour			
Potential difference (V)		around 0	
Use			Stops appliance casing becoming live.

Current only flows through _____ when there's a fault.

Electric Shocks

[_____] produced across body.

 through body.

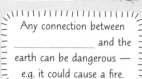

Electric shocks can [_____].

Even if a plug socket [_____], there is still danger of an electric shock.

Any connection between _____ and the earth can be dangerous — e.g. it could cause a fire.

Topic P2 — Electricity

| Second Go: ..... / ..... / ..... | **Electricity in the Home** |

Two Types of Electricity Supply

(1) ALTERNATING CURRENT (   ) —

(2) DIRECT CURRENT (   ) —

Three Facts about UK Mains

(1)

(2)

(3)

Three-core Cables

-
-

.... (green and yellow)

.... (blue)

.... (brown)

Colour			
Potential difference (V)			
Use			

⎯⎯⎯⎯ only flows through ⎯⎯⎯⎯ when there's a ⎯⎯⎯.

Electric Shocks

Current flows through body.

Electric shocks can

Even if a plug socket

Energy, Power and the National Grid

Energy Transfers

When charge flows, ⟨_____⟩ (and so energy is transferred).

Energy transferred _____ to _____ of the heating element inside the kettle.

Energy transferred _____ to _____ of the fan's motor.

Energy

potential difference (V)

⟨_____⟩ (J) $E =$ ⟨_____⟩ charge flow (C)

Amount of energy an appliance transfers depends on:

•

•

⟨_____⟩ (J)

$E = Pt$ ⟨_____⟩ (W) — time (s)

Power

POWER — ⟨_____⟩.

POWER RATING — maximum safe power ⟨_____⟩.

⟨_____⟩ (W) potential difference (V)

$P = VI$ ⟨_____⟩ (A)

⟨_____⟩ (W)

$P = I^2R$ ⟨_____⟩ (A) ⟨_____⟩ (Ω)

The National Grid

NATIONAL GRID — a system of ⟨_____⟩ and ⟨_____⟩ that connect power stations to consumers.

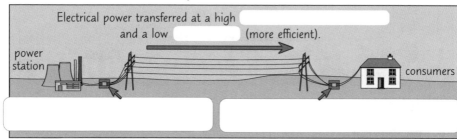

Electrical power transferred at a high ⟨_____⟩ and a low ⟨_____⟩ (more efficient).

power station

consumers

Transferring at a high ⟨_____⟩ would heat up the wires and transfer a lot of energy to the ⟨_____⟩ of the surroundings (not efficient).

Energy, Power and the National Grid

Energy Transfers

When charge flows, ⬚ is done (and so energy is transferred).

of
the heating element inside the kettle.

of the fan's motor.

Energy

energy transferred (J)

⬚ | ⬚

⬚

Amount of ⬚
transfers depends on:

-
-

⬚

$E = Pt$ ⬚

Power

POWER —

POWER RATING —

⬚

$P = $ ⬚
current (A)

⬚

⬚
resistance (Ω)

The National Grid

NATIONAL GRID —

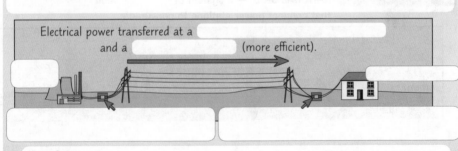

Electrical power transferred at a ⬚
and a ⬚ (more efficient).

Transferring at a ⬚

 ✓ ✓ ✓

Mixed Practice Quizzes

I hope you're not too frazzled from pages 215-220, because it's time to power through some quiz questions. Give them a go, mark your test, and see how you did.

Quiz 1 — Date: ...... / ...... / ......

1) State the purpose of a step-up transformer in the national grid. ☑

2) What is the equation that links energy transferred, charge flow and potential difference? ☑

3) What happens to the total resistance of a circuit when another resistor is added to the circuit in series? ☑

4) What is meant by the power rating of a device? ☑

5) True or false? It can be dangerous to touch an exposed wire even if its plug is turned off. ☑

6) What is meant by alternating current? ☑

7) What is the voltage of the UK mains supply? ☑

8) What is the purpose of the earth wire in an appliance? ☑

9) What electrical property is the same on every branch of a parallel circuit? ☑

10) True or false? The frequency of the UK mains supply is 230 Hz. ☑

Total:

Quiz 2 — Date: ...... / ...... / ......

1) What is the national grid? ☑

2) True or false? The UK mains supply provides direct current. ☑

3) What is the potential difference of the live wire in a UK plug? ☑

4) Describe one energy transfer that occurs when an electric kettle is used. ☑

5) How does adding a resistor in parallel affect the total resistance of a circuit? ☑

6) In what type of circuit is the current the same at every point in the circuit? ☑

7) State two factors that determine the amount of energy transferred by an appliance. ☑

8) State the equation that links power, current and resistance. ☑

9) How do you calculate the total resistance of two resistors connected in series? ☑

10) What colour is the live wire in a three-core cable? ☑

Total:

Mixed Practice Quizzes

Quiz 3   Date: ...... / ...... / ......

1) What device is used to decrease the potential difference of the electricity supply in the national grid?

2) What electrical property is the same everywhere in a series circuit?

3) During an electric shock, what happens after a large potential difference is formed across the body?

4) What type of current always flows in the same direction?

5) What is the potential difference of the earth wire in a UK plug?

6) What value is equal to energy transferred per second?

7) True or false? The earth wire only carries current if there is a fault.

8) True or false? Adding another resistor in parallel increases the total resistance of the circuit.

9) What could happen if there is a connection between the live wire and the earth?

10) Give two equations for power in an electrical circuit.

Total:

Quiz 4   Date: ...... / ...... / ......

1) Why is electrical power transmitted at a low current in the national grid?

2) What is the frequency of the UK mains supply?

3) State the equation that links power, potential difference and current.

4) True or false? Adding a resistor in series increases the total resistance of the circuit.

5) What colour is the neutral wire in a three-core cable?

6) What type of current is constantly changing direction?

7) What is the purpose of the live wire in a three-core cable?

8) Why are the wires of a three-core cable colour coded?

9) True or false? The total resistance of two resistors in parallel is less than the resistance of the smaller of the two resistors.

10) In what type of circuit is the total source potential difference shared between components?

Total:

The Particle Model & Motion in Gases

States of Matter

Density ↓

	Particle arrangement	Forces between particles	Distance between particles	Particle motion
SOLID		Strong		Vibration only
LIQUID	Irregular	Weak		
GAS			Large	

Gas Particles and Gas Pressure

Gas particles are _____ .

The higher the _____ of a gas, the higher
the _____ in the kinetic energy
stores of the gas particles.

Gas pressure is caused by _____
_____
with a surface and exerting a
_____ .

Net force

A Gas at Constant Volume

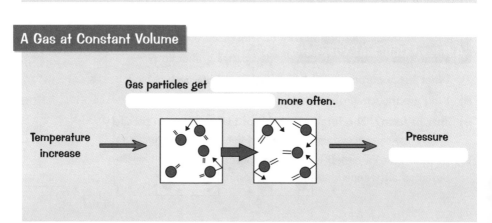

Gas particles get _____
_____ more often.

Temperature increase →

Pressure
_____

The Particle Model & Motion in Gases

States of Matter

	Particle arrangement	Forces between particles	Distance between particles	Particle motion
SOLID				
LIQUID				
GAS				

Gas Particles and Gas Pressure

The higher the temperature of a gas,

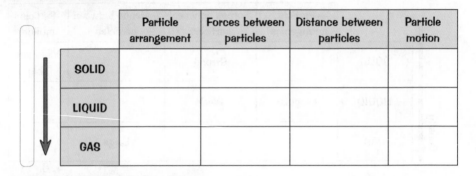

Net force

A Gas at Constant Volume

Gas particles get faster and

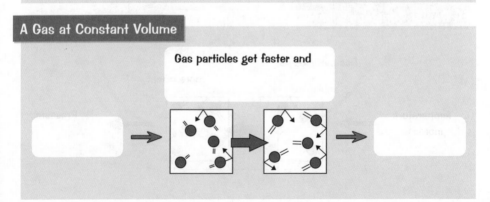

Density, Internal Energy and States

Density

DENSITY —

$$\rho = \frac{m}{V}$$

mass (kg)

volume ( )

Internal Energy

INTERNAL ENERGY — the total energy stored by the that make up a .

Internal energy of a system
= total

in

energy stores of all its particles

Heating

Heating increases the of a system.

This can do one of two things:

1 Increase the

2 Change the

Changes of State

Changes of state are . is always conserved.

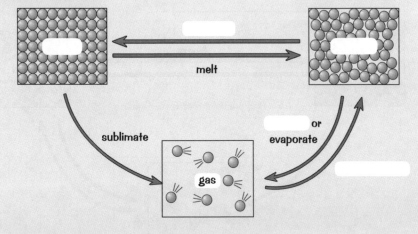

melt

sublimate

or
evaporate

gas

Density, Internal Energy and States

Density

DENSITY —

density (kg/m³)

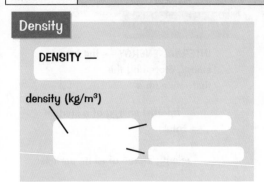

Internal Energy

INTERNAL ENERGY —

Internal energy of a system =

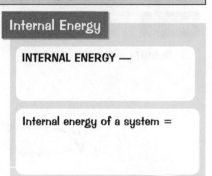

Heating

Heating increases

This can do one of two things:

1

2

Changes of State

Changes of state ....

....

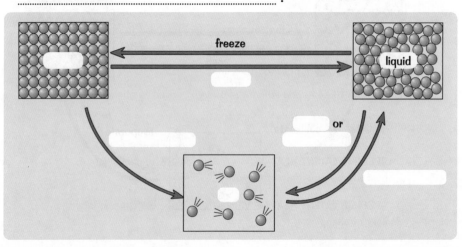

freeze

liquid

or

Heating and Cooling

Heating Graphs

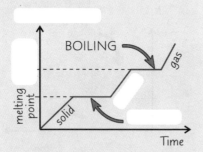

BOILING

gas

melting point

solid

Time

Three things happen in melting and boiling:

1. _____ between particles are broken.

2. Internal energy increases — energy is transferred _____ .

3. Temperature _____ .

Cooling Graphs

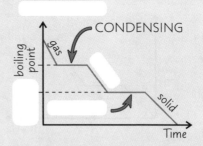

CONDENSING

boiling point

gas

solid

Time

Three things happen in condensing and freezing:

1. Stronger _____ between particles.

2. Internal energy decreases — energy is transferred _____ .

3. Temperature _____ .

Specific Heat Capacity, Latent Heat and Specific Latent Heat

SPECIFIC HEAT CAPACITY — the amount of energy needed to raise _____ .

LATENT HEAT — the energy needed to _____ .

SPECIFIC LATENT HEAT — the amount of energy needed to change _____ , without changing _____ .

SPECIFIC LATENT HEAT OF _____ — the specific latent heat of changing between a solid _____ .

SPECIFIC LATENT HEAT OF VAPORISATION — the specific latent heat of changing _____ .

Topic P3 — Particle Model of Matter

Heating and Cooling

Heating Graphs

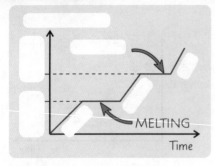

Cooling Graphs

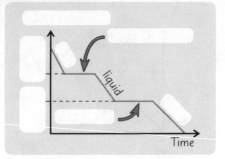

Three things happen in melting and boiling:

3

Three things happen in condensing and freezing:

3

Specific Heat Capacity, Latent Heat and Specific Latent Heat

SPECIFIC HEAT CAPACITY —

LATENT HEAT —

SPECIFIC LATENT HEAT —

SPECIFIC LATENT HEAT OF FUSION —

SPECIFIC LATENT HEAT OF VAPORISATION —

Mixed Practice Quizzes

Keep your cool — have a go at these quiz questions which test you on pages 223-228. Tick off the questions you get right to work out your total.

Quiz 1 Date: ...... / ...... / ......

1) True or false? The internal energy of a system is equal to the total energy in the kinetic energy stores of the particles. ☑

2) Does an upwards slope on a heating graph show a temperature change or a change in state? ☑

3) State what happens to the temperature of a substance as it condenses. ☑

4) Which usually has a lower density — a solid or a liquid? ☑

5) What is meant by latent heat? ☑

6) Give the formula for density. ☑

7) True or false? Mass is always conserved during changes of state. ☑

8) Which state of matter has the biggest distance between its particles? ☑

9) What happens to the internal energy of a gas when the gas is heated? ☑

10) What causes gas pressure? ☑

Total:

Quiz 2 Date: ...... / ...... / ......

1) Explain what happens to the pressure of a gas if you increase its temperature whilst keeping it at a constant volume. ☑

2) Between which two states of matter does freezing occur? ☑

3) What happens to the internal energy of a substance as it condenses? ☑

4) Give the definition of specific latent heat. ☑

5) True or false? Changes of state are chemical changes. ☑

6) Give the definition of specific heat capacity. ☑

7) Which has a higher density — a liquid or a gas? ☑

8) Describe the particle motion of particles in a solid. ☑

9) In what state of matter are the forces between particles weakest? ☑

10) True or false? The flat parts of a heating graph show a change of state. ☑

Total:

Mixed Practice Quizzes

Quiz 3   Date: ...... / ...... / ......

1) What is the difference between specific heat capacity and specific latent heat? ☑

2) True or false? Heating a substance always increases its temperature. ☑

3) Name the term given for a gas turning into a liquid. ☑

4) Give the definition for the specific latent heat of fusion. ☑

5) In what state of matter are particles in a regular, fixed arrangement? ☑

6) State what happens to the internal energy of a substance as it boils. ☑

7) What is meant by the density of a substance? ☑

8) What is meant by the internal energy of a system? ☑

9) Does a downwards slope on a cooling graph show a temperature change or a change in state? ☑

10) Describe the motion of gas particles. ☑

Total: ☐

Quiz 4   Date: ...... / ...... / ......

1) Can increasing the internal energy of a system cause a change of state? ☑

2) Describe the particle arrangement of particles in solids, liquids and gases. ☑

3) True or false? Gas particles are constantly moving randomly. ☑

4) What is meant by sublimation? ☑

5) Give the definition for the specific latent heat of vaporisation. ☑

6) Explain what happens to the pressure of a gas if you decrease its temperature whilst keeping it at a constant volume. ☑

7) What is it called when a solid turns into a liquid? ☑

8) True or false? The melting point of a substance is the temperature at which a gas of the substance can turn into a liquid. ☑

9) What happens to the average energy in the kinetic energy stores of gas particles if the temperature of the gas is increased? ☑

10) True or false? Bonds between particles are broken when a substance is melting. ☑

Total: ☐

Topic P3 — Particle Model of Matter

Developing the Model of the Atom

First Go:
..... /..... /.....

The History of the Atom

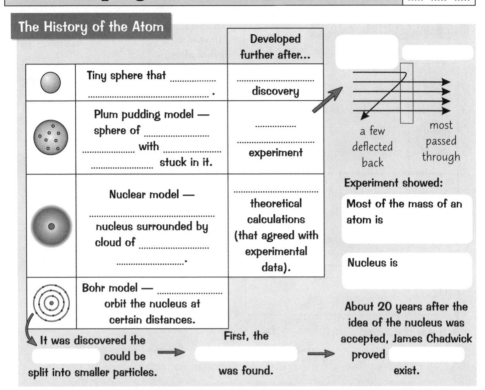

		Developed further after...	
○	Tiny sphere that	.... discovery	
(plum pudding)	Plum pudding model — sphere of .... with .... stuck in it.	.... experiment	a few deflected back most passed through
(nuclear)	Nuclear model — .... nucleus surrounded by cloud of	.... theoretical calculations (that agreed with experimental data).	Experiment showed: Most of the mass of an atom is Nucleus is
(Bohr)	Bohr model — .... orbit the nucleus at certain distances.		About 20 years after the idea of the nucleus was accepted, James Chadwick

It was discovered the
.... could be
split into smaller particles.   →   First, the
....
was found.   →   proved ....
exist.

The Current Model of the Atom

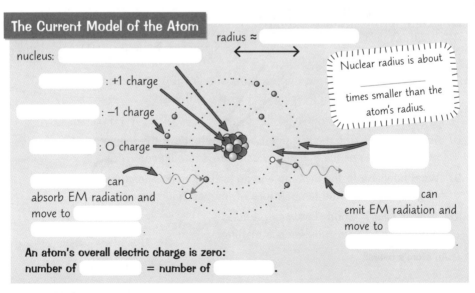

radius ≈ ....

nucleus: ....

.... : +1 charge

.... : −1 charge

.... : O charge

.... can
absorb EM radiation and
move to ....
....

Nuclear radius is about
....
times smaller than the
atom's radius.

.... can
emit EM radiation and
move to ....
....

An atom's overall electric charge is zero:
number of .... = number of ....

232

Developing the Model of the Atom

The History of the Atom

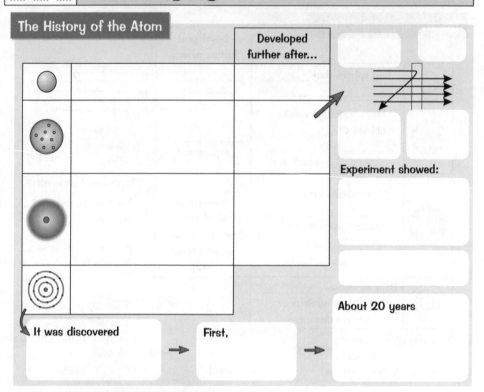

Developed further after...

Experiment showed:

About 20 years

It was discovered

First,

The Current Model of the Atom

radius ≈

radius is about

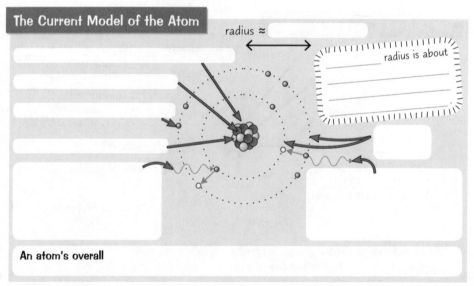

An atom's overall

Isotopes and Nuclear Radiation

Mass Number and Atomic Number

ISOTOPES of an element — atoms with the same number of _____ but different numbers of _____ .

All atoms of each element have _____
_____

_____ — total number of _____ and _____ in an atom.

$^{16}_{8}O$

_____ — number of _____ in an atom (equal to _____ of nucleus).

Types of Nuclear Radiation

RADIOACTIVE DECAY — when an unstable nucleus _____ into _____ and gives out _____ to become more stable.

IONISING RADIATION (α, β and γ) — radiation that knocks _____ off atoms, creating _____ .

	_____ (α)	_____ (β)	_____ (γ)
Consists of...	2 _____ and 2 _____ (_____ nucleus)	fast-moving _____ from _____ nucleus	_____ from nucleus
Absorbed by...	Sheet of _____	Sheet of _____	Thick sheets of _____
Range in air	Few _____	Few _____	
Ionising power		Moderate	
Example of use			Medical tracers

Unstable nuclei can also release _____ when they decay.

234

Isotopes and Nuclear Radiation

Mass Number and Atomic Number

ISOTOPES of an element —

All atoms of each element _____

$^{16}_{8}O$

Types of Nuclear Radiation

RADIOACTIVE DECAY —

IONISING RADIATION (α, β and γ) —

	(α)	(β)	(γ)
Consists of...			
Absorbed by...			
Range in air			
Ionising power			
Example of use			

Unstable nuclei can also

Topic P4 — Atomic Structure

Nuclear Radiation and Half-life

Nuclear Equations

α-decay

$$^{238}_{92}U \longrightarrow Th + ^4_2He$$

- mass ....
- charge ....

γ-decay
- mass and charge ....
  ....

β-decay

$$^{14}_{6}C \longrightarrow N + ^0_{-1}e$$

- mass ....
- charge ....

During _____, a neutron in the nucleus turns into a _____.

Activity and Count-Rate

ACTIVITY — the ____ at which a source ____, measured in becquerels (Bq).

COUNT-RATE — the ____

reaching a detector ____.

A Geiger-Muller tube and counter measure ____.

Half-life

Radioactive decay is ____.

HALF-LIFE — time taken for ____ to halve.

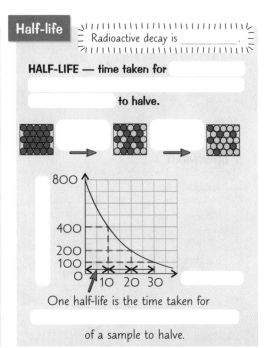

One half-life is the time taken for ____

of a sample to halve.

Topic P4 — Atomic Structure

Nuclear Radiation and Half-life

Nuclear Equations

α-decay

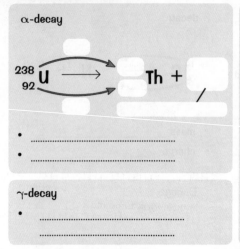

$$\begin{array}{c} 238 \\ 92 \end{array} U \longrightarrow \boxed{} Th + \boxed{}$$

- ....
- ....

β-decay

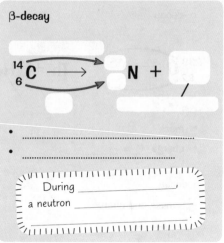

$$\begin{array}{c} 14 \\ 6 \end{array} C \longrightarrow \boxed{} N + \boxed{}$$

- ....
- ....

During ....,
a neutron ....
....

γ-decay

- ....
....

Activity and Count-Rate

ACTIVITY —

COUNT-RATE —

A .... and counter measure ....

Half-life

Radioactive decay is ....

HALF-LIFE —

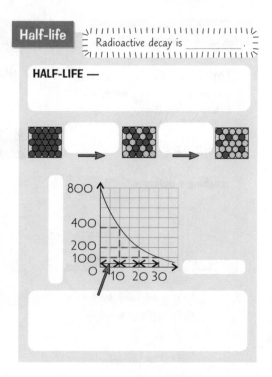

Contamination, Irradiation and Risk

Contamination and Irradiation

RADIOACTIVE
CONTAMINATION
— getting unwanted
radioactive atoms

IRRADIATION — the

to nuclear radiation

(

).

Three precautions to protect against _____ :

(1) Keep sources in _____ .

(2) _____ barriers or be in _____ to the source.

(3) _____ with remote-controlled arms.

Risk of Radiation

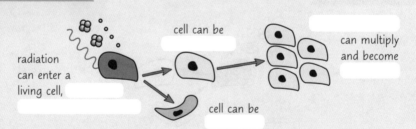

radiation
can enter a
living cell,

cell can be

cell can be

can multiply
and become

Inside body:
- .... is most dangerous
- .... is least dangerous

Outside body:
- .... is most dangerous
- .... is least dangerous

Second Go: ..... / ..... / ..... | Contamination, Irradiation and Risk

Contamination and Irradiation

RADIOACTIVE CONTAMINATION —

IRRADIATION —

Three precautions to protect against irradiation:

1

2

3

Risk of Radiation

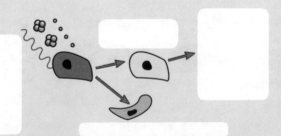

Inside body:
- .... is most dangerous
- .... is least dangerous

Outside body:
- .... is most dangerous
- .... is least dangerous

Topic P4 — Atomic Structure

Mixed Practice Quizzes

Before all that revision from p.231-238 decays out of your brain, try these quizzes.
When you finish each quiz, check your answers and work out your score.

Quiz 1 | Date: ...... / ...... / ......

1) True or false? The mass of a nucleus
   decreases when it emits an alpha particle.

2) What is meant by the activity of a radioactive source?

3) Which model of the atom was adopted after the plum pudding model?

4) True or false? The nucleus of an atom is negatively charged.

5) Which type of ionising radiation has the longest range in air?

6) What is the approximate radius of an atom?

7) What is beta radiation made up of?

8) What name is given to the number of protons in an atom?

9) Which type of ionising radiation is most dangerous inside the body?

10) What can be used to measure the count-rate of a radioactive source?

Total:

Quiz 2 | Date: ...... / ...... / ......

1) What does an electron need to absorb to
   move to a higher energy level in an atom?

2) What are isotopes of an element?

3) True or false? An unstable nucleus may decay by emitting a neutron.

4) What evidence caused the nuclear model of the atom
   to develop into the Bohr model of the atom?

5) Which type of nuclear radiation is made up of a helium nucleus?

6) What is meant by irradiation?

7) True or false? Half-life is equal to the time taken for
   the activity of a sample to fall to half of its initial level.

8) What is meant by ionising radiation?

9) What happens to the charge on a nucleus when it emits a beta particle?

10) What experiment disproved the plum pudding model of the atom?

Total:

Mixed Practice Quizzes

Quiz 3   Date: ...... / ...... / ......

1) True or false? When a nucleus emits
gamma radiation, its charge decreases.

2) What does a Geiger-Muller tube and counter measure?

3) What is the overall electric charge of an atom?

4) What did the alpha particle scattering experiment prove about the atom?

5) What name is given to the time taken for the number
of nuclei of an isotope in a sample to halve?

6) How many times smaller is the radius of a
nucleus compared to the radius of an atom?

7) What does the mass number of an atom tell you?

8) Give one precaution you could take to protect against irradiation.

9) True or false? Beta radiation has a shorter range in air
than gamma radiation.

10) Which type of nuclear radiation has the highest ionising power?

Total:

Quiz 4   Date: ...... / ...... / ......

1) True or false? All atoms of the same element
have the same number of neutrons.

2) How does the charge of a nucleus change when it emits an alpha particle?

3) What two particles make up the nucleus of an atom?

4) What is meant by radioactive decay?

5) Which type of nuclear radiation is absorbed by a sheet of paper?

6) True or false? Electrons are negatively charged.

7) During which type of radioactive decay does
a neutron in the nucleus turn into a proton?

8) Who proved the existence of the neutron?

9) What is meant by radioactive contamination?

10) Describe the plum pudding model of the atom.

Total:

Scalars, Vectors and Forces

Scalars

SCALAR QUANTITIES —

-
- distance
-
- mass
-

Vectors

VECTOR QUANTITIES —

- force
-
- acceleration

Direction of arrow shows
....
....
Length of arrow shows
....

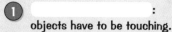

Forces

FORCE — a push or a pull on an object caused by

Two types of forces:

1 :
objects have to be touching.

-
- tension
-
- normal contact force

2 :
objects don't need to be touching.

- gravitational force
-
-

Second Go:
...../...../.....

Scalars, Vectors and Forces

Scalars

SCALAR QUANTITIES —

-
-
-
-
- time

Vectors

VECTOR QUANTITIES —

-
-

Direction of

Forces

FORCE — a push or a pull on an object

Two types of forces:

1

- friction
-
-
-

2

-
-
- magnetic force

Weight, Resultant Forces & Work Done

Weight, Mass and Gravity

WEIGHT — force that acts on an object due to [   ].

Near Earth, weight is caused by [   ]
[   ].

Measure weight with [   ]

weight (N)

[   ]

$W = mg$

[   ]

⸿ Weight and mass are [   ] ⸿

CENTRE OF MASS — point at which an object's [   ] [   ] to act.

- Object weight depends on [   ] of gravitational field at object location.
- [   ] has same value anywhere in the universe.

Resultant Force

RESULTANT FORCE —
a [   ] force that can [   ]
[   ] on an object to give the [   ] as all the original forces acting together.

Add forces pointing in [   ].

Subtract forces pointing in [   ].

F_1 F_2

[   ] = resultant force

EQUILIBRIUM — when the forces acting on an object are [   ] and the resultant force [   ].

Work Done

When a force moves an object from one point to another, energy is [   ] and work is done on the object.

work done (J)
(1 joule = [   ])

$W = $ [ ] s

force (N)

distance (moved along [   ]) (m)

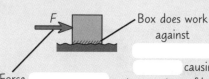

Box does work against

[   ] causing temperature of box to increase.

Force [   ] on box and energy is transferred to box's [   ] energy store.

Weight, Resultant Forces & Work Done

Weight, Mass and Gravity

WEIGHT —

Near Earth,

$W =$

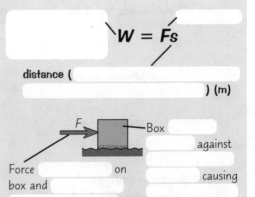

Measure weight with

CENTRE OF MASS —

- Object weight

- Object mass

Resultant Force

RESULTANT FORCE — a single force that can

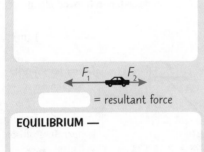

= resultant force

EQUILIBRIUM —

Work Done

When a force moves an object from one point to another,

$$W = Fs$$

distance ( ) (m)

Box

against

Force   on box and   causing

to box's energy store.

Forces and Elasticity

Changing Shape

_____ to act
on a stationary object to change its shape.

_____

stretch

F

F

F

F

F

F

F

Two Types of Deformation

1 **ELASTIC** — object goes back
to _____
_____ after
forces have been removed.

Elastic objects can be
_____
_____ .

2 **INELASTIC** — object doesn't go
back to _____
_____
_____ .

Force-Extension Relationship for an Elastic Object

extension or
_____ (m)

____ $= ke$

____ (N)

spring constant
(____)

Extension of a stretched
spring is _____
_____ to
load or force applied.
Graph is _____ .

limit of _____

Force

Force gets _____ — extension no longer
_____ .

Graph is _____ .

Work Done and Elasticity

Force ....
or ....
object.

→ .... →

Energy transferred to object's
....
....

In elastic deformation, _____
_____ to object's elastic
potential energy store.

The larger the _____
_____ *, the more energy*
transferred to object's _____
_____ .

Forces and Elasticity

Changing Shape

More than one ....
....
....

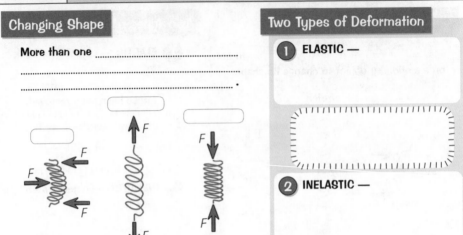

Two Types of Deformation

1 ELASTIC —

2 INELASTIC —

Force-Extension Relationship for an Elastic Object

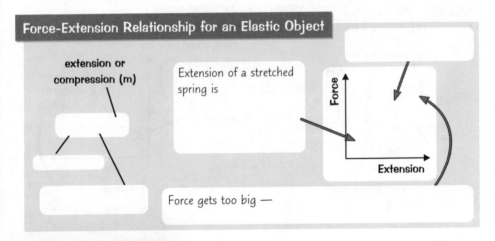

extension or
compression (m)

Extension of a stretched
spring is

Force gets too big —

Force ↑ Extension →

Work Done and Elasticity

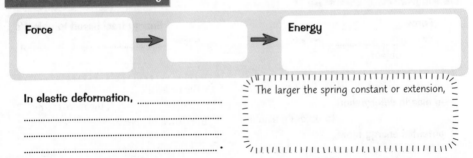

Force → → Energy

In elastic deformation, ...
....
....
....

The larger the spring constant or extension,

Mixed Practice Quizzes

Get some good work done by testing yourself with some questions on p.241-246.

Quiz 1   Date: ...... / ...... / ......

1) Give two examples of contact forces.

2) The shape of an object can be changed by bending or stretching the object. Give one other way that the shape of an object can be changed.

3) What does the direction of a vector arrow tell you about the vector quantity?

4) Apart from its mass, what does the weight of an object depend on?

5) How do you calculate the resultant force of two forces pointing in the same direction?

6) True or false? Scalar quantities have a magnitude and a direction.

7) What are the units for work done?

8) Which energy store is energy transferred to in elastic deformation?

9) What is a spring constant measured in?

10) True or false? The forces acting on an object in equilibrium are balanced.

Total:

Quiz 2   Date: ...... / ...... / ......

1) True or false? When an object does work against frictional forces, it causes the temperature of the object to increase.

2) Give two examples of non-contact forces.

3) What is meant by a resultant force?

4) Does the amount of energy stored in the elastic potential energy store of an object increase or decrease with an increase in the object's extension?

5) Describe the difference between scalar and vector quantities.

6) What is the equation for calculating the work done by a force on an object?

7) What is the name for the force that acts on an object due to gravity?

8) Describe the shape of a force-extension graph for an elastic object.

9) True or false? Only one force has to act on a stationary object to change its shape.

10) What is meant by the centre of mass of an object?

Total:

Mixed Practice Quizzes

Date: ...... / ...... / ......

1) What type of force does the gravitational field around Earth cause? ☑

2) How do you calculate the resultant force of two forces
   pointing in opposite directions to each other? ☑

3) True or false? Weight has the units N/kg. ☑

4) What is the equation that links force, spring constant and extension? ☑

5) Describe the difference between contact and non-contact forces. ☑

6) Below the limit of proportionality, is the force applied to an elastic object
   directly proportional or inversely proportional to the object's extension? ☑

7) Name a piece of apparatus that can be used to measure weight. ☑

8) True or false? Work is done when a force
   moves an object from one point to another. ☑

9) Give three examples of vector quantities. ☑

10) True or false? In elastic deformation, work is done and half of the
    energy is transferred to the object's elastic potential energy store. ☑

Total: ☐

Quiz 4   Date: ...... / ...... / ......

1) What is a force? ☑

2) Give the equation for calculating the weight of an object,
   defining each symbol used. ☑

3) What two things can the e stand for in the formula $F = ke$? ☑

4) Does a graph showing the force-extension relationship of an elastic object
   become linear or non-linear after the limit of proportionality? ☑

5) What is meant by the weight of an object? ☑

6) What does the length of a vector arrow tell you about the vector quantity? ☑

7) True or false? The weight and mass of an object are directly proportional. ☑

8) What is the resultant force acting on an object in equilibrium? ☑

9) Describe the difference between elastic and inelastic deformation. ☑

10) 1 newton metre is equal to how many joules of work? ☑

Total: ☐

Motion

Distance and Displacement

DISTANCE (scalar) —
[_____]
[_____]
(not including its
[_____]).

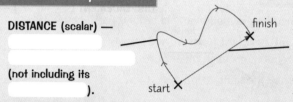

finish

start

DISPLACEMENT (vector) —
the [_____] and the
[_____] from
an object's starting point
to its finishing point.

Speed and Velocity

SPEED (scalar) — how [_____] you're
going with no regard to [_____].

VELOCITY ([_____] **) —** [_____]
in a certain [_____].

[_____] [___] = **vt**
(m)

time (s)

speed ([___])

People's walking, running and
cycling speed can be affected by:

- [_____]

- age

- [_____]

- type of ground

	Typical speed (m/s)
	1.5
running	
	6
a car	
	30
a plane	
sound	

Objects, _____
rarely travel at a constant speed.

Acceleration

ACCELERATION — the
[_____]
in a certain amount of [_____].

Deceleration is [_____]
(shows an object is [_____]).

Acceleration of object due to gravity close to Earth's surface
(object in [_____]) is roughly [_____].

acceleration
([___]) — $a = \dfrac{\Delta v}{t}$

change in
[_____]
(m/s)

(s)

 ☑ ☑ ☑

Topic P5 — Forces

Motion

Distance and Displacement

DISTANCE ( ) —

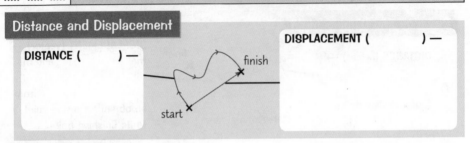

finish

start

DISPLACEMENT ( ) —

Speed and Velocity

SPEED ( ) —

VELOCITY ( ) —

$s =$

People's , and
speed can be affected by:

-
-
- distance travelled
-

	Typical speed (m/s)
walking	
cycling	
a train	

Objects, sound and wind rarely travel
....

Acceleration

ACCELERATION —

(m/s^2)

change in velocity ( )

Deceleration is

Acceleration of object due to gravity

251

Distance-Time & Velocity-Time Graphs

First Go: ..... / ..... / .....

Distance-Time Graphs

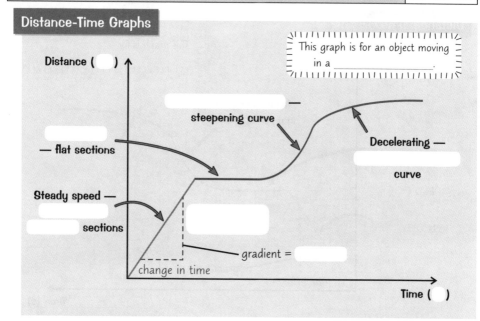

This graph is for an object moving in a _____.

Distance ( )

steepening curve

— flat sections

Decelerating — curve

Steady speed —

sections

gradient =

change in time

Time ( )

Velocity-Time Graphs

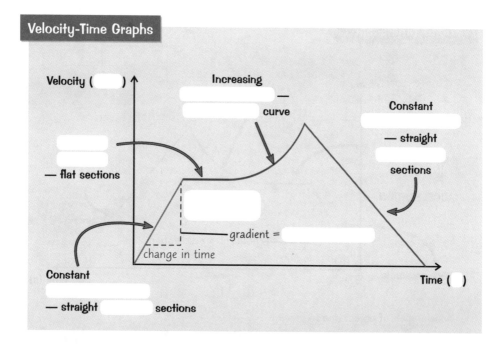

Velocity ( )

Increasing —

curve

Constant — straight sections

— flat sections

gradient =

change in time

Constant — straight sections

Time ( )

Topic P5 — Forces

Distance-Time & Velocity-Time Graphs

Distance-Time Graphs

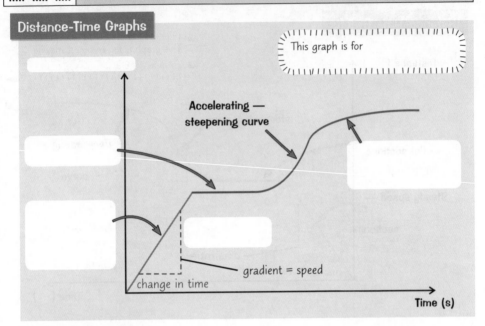

This graph is for

Accelerating —
steepening curve

gradient = speed

change in time

Time (s)

Velocity-Time Graphs

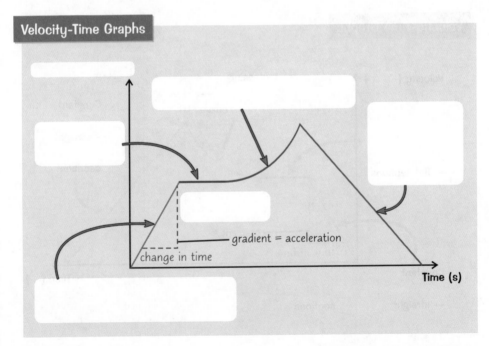

gradient = acceleration

change in time

Time (s)

Topic P5 — Forces

Newton's Laws of Motion

Newton's First Law

If [ ] resultant force acts on stationary object, [ ] .

If [ ] resultant force acts on moving object, [ ]
[ ] .

driving force   resistive force

If [ ] resultant force acts on object, object [ ] (will change [ ], [ ]).

Newton's Second Law

resultant force ( )   mass ( )

$$F = \frac{}{}$$

acceleration ( )

• Acceleration is [ ] to resultant force — [ ] .
• Acceleration is [ ] to mass.

Newton's Third Law

Two interacting objects exert .... forces on each other.

Rocket exhaust gas pushed [ ] by rocket.

Causes [ ] and [ ] force as gas [ ] on rocket.

Rocket moves when [ ] is greater than [ ] .

Girl [ ] on wall.

— wall pushes back on girl with [ ] and [ ] force.

Topic P5 — Forces

Newton's Laws of Motion

Newton's First Law

If zero resultant force acts on stationary object,

If zero resultant force acts on moving object,

force   force

If non-zero resultant force acts on object,

Newton's Second Law

mass (kg)

$$F = ma$$

- Acceleration is

- Acceleration is

Newton's Third Law

Two interacting objects ....
....

Rocket exhaust gas pushed

Causes

and

as gas

on rocket.

Girl pushes on wall.

Terminal Velocity and Reaction Times

Terminal Velocity

FRICTION — a force that acts to

_____ . It always acts

_____

_____ .

DRAG — the frictional force caused by any _____ on a _____ (e.g. _____).

Frictional forces from fluids always _____ .

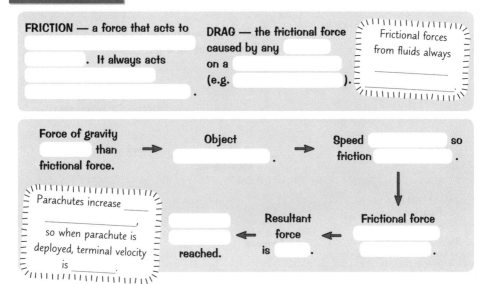

Force of gravity _____ than frictional force.

→ Object _____ .

→ Speed _____ so friction _____ .

↓

Frictional force _____ .

Resultant force is _____ .

_____ _____ reached.

Parachutes increase _____ _____ , so when parachute is deployed, terminal velocity is _____ .

Reaction Times

Typical reaction time: _____ .

Three factors affecting reaction times:

1 _____

2 _____

3 _____

_____ affect your ability to react.

The Ruler Drop Test

Three steps to investigate reaction time:

1 Get someone to hold _____ so _____ is between your _____ .

2 _____ dropped without _____ . _____ as _____ as possible.

3 Use _____ to _____ reaction time.

The _____ _____ , the longer the reaction time.

Topic P5 — Forces

Terminal Velocity and Reaction Times

Terminal Velocity

FRICTION —

DRAG — the frictional force caused by any

Frictional forces

Force

→ Object accelerates. →

Speed

Parachutes increase air resistance, so

Terminal

←

←

Reaction Times

Typical reaction time: .

Three factors affecting reaction times:

① ② ③

affect your

The Ruler Drop Test

Three steps to investigate reaction time:

①

②

③

The longer the distance,

Stopping Distances

Stopping Distance Equation

Stopping distance = _____ + _____

How far vehicle moves during _____ .

Distance taken to stop whilst _____ .

Two factors that increase thinking distance:

1 _____

2 slower driver _____

Four factors that increase braking distance:

1 faster vehicle _____

2 _____ weather

3 poor road _____

4 damaged or worn _____

Speed (mph)	30		
Typical stopping distance (m)		73	

The bigger the _____ _____, the more _____ drivers need to leave between their car and the _____ .

Work Done When Stopping

Driver _____, causing brake pads to be _____ onto wheels.

⬇

_____ between them causes _____ .

⬇

Energy _____ from _____ energy stores of wheels to _____ energy stores of brakes.

⬇

Brakes _____ .

Large Decelerations

The _____ a vehicle is going, the _____ the _____ needed to make it stop in a certain distance.

⬇

Larger braking force means larger _____ .

Very large deceleration can cause:

• brakes _____

• vehicle _____

 ✓   ✓   ✓

Topic P5 — Forces

Stopping Distances

Stopping Distance Equation

Stopping distance = Thinking Distance + Braking Distance

Two factors that increase thinking distance:

1.
2.

Four factors that increase braking distance:

1. faster vehicle speed
2.
3.
4.

Speed (mph)			
Typical stopping distance (m)			

The bigger the stopping distance,

Work Done When Stopping

Driver brakes,

↓

Friction

↓

Energy transferred from kinetic energy stores

↓

Brakes

Large Decelerations

The faster a vehicle is going,

in a certain distance.

↓

Very large deceleration can cause:

•
•

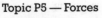

Mixed Practice Quizzes

Hit the brakes before you go any further and try these quizzes covering p.249-258.

Quiz 1 | Date: ...... / ...... / ......

1) True or false? A larger braking force means a larger deceleration.
2) What does each symbol in $s = vt$ stand for?
3) What does the gradient of a distance-time graph tell you about an object?
4) The stopping distance of a vehicle is the sum of the thinking distance and what other distance?
5) What is meant by the velocity of an object?
6) What are the units of acceleration?
7) True or false? According to Newton's Second Law, acceleration is inversely proportional to resultant force.
8) Give two factors that increase thinking distance.
9) Describe an experiment you could do to investigate someone's reaction time.
10) When a vehicle is travelling at a steady speed, is the driving force the same as or different to the resistive force?

Total:

Quiz 2 | Date: ...... / ...... / ......

1) What is Newton's Third Law?
2) Name three factors that affect reaction times.
3) What is the resultant force acting on an object falling at its terminal velocity?
4) Give a typical speed for a person: a) walking, b) running, c) cycling.
5) True or false? The faster a vehicle is going, the greater the braking force needed to stop it in a certain distance.
6) What is meant by the braking distance of a vehicle?
7) Give the equation for Newton's Second Law.
8) True or false? Moving objects often travel at a constant speed.
9) What is meant by the displacement of an object?
10) What does a flat section of a velocity-time graph represent?

Total:

Mixed Practice Quizzes

Quiz 3

Date: ...... / ...... / ......

1) What does the gradient of a velocity-time graph tell you about an object?

2) True or false? The acceleration of an object due to gravity close to the Earth's surface is roughly 12.8 m/s².

3) True or false? Distance is a scalar quantity.

4) What is meant by thinking distance?

5) Give a typical human reaction time.

6) Does the friction acting on an object work in the same direction or the opposite direction to its movement?

7) Why can large decelerations be dangerous?

8) Give three factors that can affect a person's cycling speed.

9) True or false? The speed of sound and the speed of wind are constant.

10) What is a typical stopping distance for a car travelling at 60 mph?

Total:

Quiz 4

Date: ...... / ...... / ......

1) True or false? Velocity and speed are vector quantities.

2) If a zero resultant force acts on a moving object, does the velocity of the object change or stay the same?

3) Give two factors that increase the braking distance of a vehicle.

4) True or false? Distractions can affect your ability to react.

5) What is meant by "deceleration"?

6) Explain why the brakes heat up when a vehicle is braking.

7) What does a straight uphill section of a distance-time graph represent?

8) If a person with a slow reaction time does the ruler drop test, will the ruler fall a short way or a long way before they catch it?

9) True or false? The greater the speed of a vehicle, the greater its stopping distance.

10) What is the speed of sound in air?

Total:

Transverse and Longitudinal Waves

Wave Basics

When waves travel through a medium, they ⬚ ⬚ .

Sound waves move away...

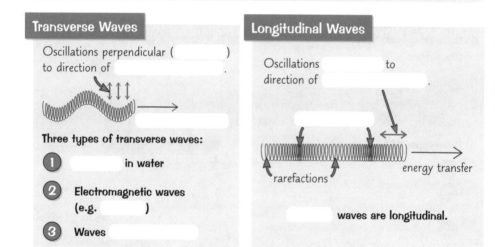

Ripples on water's surface move away...

...

...

FREQUENCY — number of ⬚ ⬚ passing a certain point ⬚ .

PERIOD — amount of time it takes for a ⬚ .

AMPLITUDE — ⬚ of a point on a wave from ⬚ .

Displacement

Distance (m)

WAVELENGTH — length of ⬚

Transverse Waves

Oscillations perpendicular (⬚) to direction of ⬚ .

⬚

Three types of transverse waves:

1 ⬚ in water

2 Electromagnetic waves (e.g. ⬚)

3 Waves ⬚

Longitudinal Waves

Oscillations ⬚ to direction of ⬚ .

⬚

rarefactions

energy transfer

⬚ waves are longitudinal.

The Wave Equation

WAVE SPEED — speed at which a ⬚ ⬚ (or speed ⬚).

1 Hz is ⬚ .

frequency (⬚ , Hz)

wave speed (⬚) —— $v = $ ⬚ λ —— ⬚ (m)

 ✓ ✓ ✓

Transverse and Longitudinal Waves

Wave Basics

When waves travel

Sound waves

Ripples

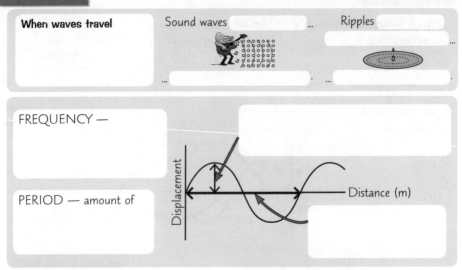

FREQUENCY —

PERIOD — amount of

Displacement — *Distance (m)*

Transverse Waves

Oscillations

to

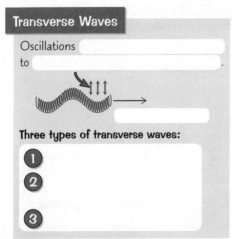

Three types of transverse waves:

1
2
3

Longitudinal Waves

Oscillations to

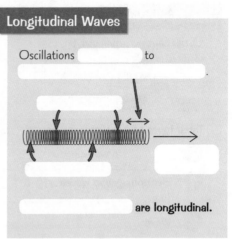

are longitudinal.

The Wave Equation

WAVE SPEED —

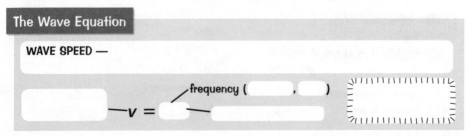

frequency (,)

$v =$

Speed of Sound, Refraction & EM Waves

Measuring the Speed of Sound

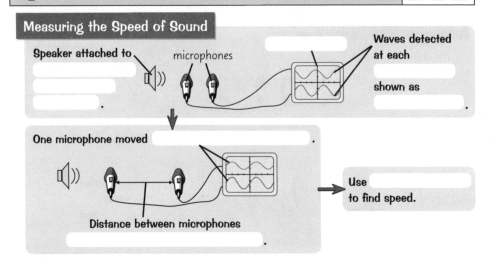

Speaker attached to [_____]

microphones

Waves detected at each [_____]

shown as [_____].

One microphone moved [_____].

Use [_____] to find speed.

Distance between microphones [_____].

Refraction

REFRACTION — when a wave [_____] as it crosses a boundary between two materials at an angle to the normal.

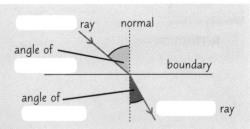

ray   normal

angle of [_____]

boundary

angle of [_____]

[_____] ray

The Electromagnetic (EM) Spectrum

The EM spectrum is ....

	Microwaves		Visible light	Ultraviolet		

Increasing [_____], decreasing [_____]

EM waves:
- Are [_____].
- Transfer energy from source [_____].
- Travel at same speed in [_____].

EM waves created and absorbed over [_____] due to changes in atoms [_____].

Our eyes can only detect ....

created by changes in atom's nucleus.

Topic P6 — Waves

Speed of Sound, Refraction & EM Waves

Measuring the Speed of Sound

oscilloscope

Waves detected

One

Use _____ to find _____ .

Refraction

REFRACTION —

incoming ray

boundary

ray

The Electromagnetic (EM) Spectrum

			Visible light			

EM waves:
- Are transverse.
-
-

EM waves _____ due to _____ .

Our eyes can only detect

_____ created by _____ .

Topic P6 — Waves

Uses and Dangers of EM Waves

Uses of EM Waves

Radio waves

- [_____]
- TV

Microwaves

- Satellite [_____]
- [_____]

Infrared radiation

- [_____]
- [_____]
- Infrared [_____]

Visible light

- Communications through [_____]

Ultraviolet waves

- Energy efficient [_____]
- [_____]

X-rays and gamma rays

- Medical [_____]
- [_____]

Dangers of EM Waves

RADIATION DOSE — measure of the [_____] to body tissues due to [_____]. It is measured in sieverts.

Risk depends on:

- [_____] of dose
- Type [_____]

1 sievert (____) = [_____] millisieverts (mSv).

Type of ionising radiation	Utraviolet	X-rays and [_____]
Harmful effects on human body tissue	• Can prematurely [_____] • Increases risk of [_____]	• [_____] • Cancer

Uses and Dangers of EM Waves

Uses of EM Waves

Radio waves

- Radio
-

Microwaves

-
-

Infrared radiation

-
-
-

Visible light

-

Ultraviolet waves

-
-

X-rays and gamma rays

- Medical imaging
-

Dangers of EM Waves

RADIATION DOSE — measure of _____
_____. It is measured in sieverts.

Risk depends on:

-
-

1 sievert (Sv) =

Type of ionising radiation	Ultraviolet	X-rays and gamma rays
Harmful effects on human body tissue	• •	• •

Mixed Practice Quizzes

Don't wave goodbye to revision yet — test yourself with these questions covering p.261-266. Tick off each question you get right to keep track of your progress.

Quiz 1 | Date: ...... / ...... / ......

1) What type of EM wave has the longest wavelength?

2) How many sieverts are equal to 1000 millisieverts?

3) Is it transverse waves or longitudinal waves that have oscillations perpendicular to the direction of energy transfer?

4) Give the formula for calculating wave speed, defining each term used.

5) True or false? All EM waves travel at the same speed in a vacuum.

6) Are electromagnetic waves transverse or longitudinal?

7) True or false? Microwaves can be used in sun tan beds.

8) What type of EM wave can cause premature skin aging?

9) What is meant by the 'amplitude' of a wave?

10) Give an example of a longitudinal wave.

Total:

Quiz 2 | Date: ...... / ...... / ......

1) What is meant by the 'period' of a wave?

2) If a human body is exposed to radiation, give two things that affect the risk of harm to the body's tissues.

3) True or false? Transverse waves have compressions and rarefactions.

4) True or false? Gamma rays can be made by changes in an atom's nucleus.

5) What type of EM wave has the lowest frequency?

6) Are sound waves transverse or longitudinal?

7) What can microwaves and infrared radiation both be used for?

8) True or false? Human eyes can detect all parts of the electromagnetic spectrum.

9) What are the units of frequency?

10) Give one use of X-rays and gamma rays.

Total:

Mixed Practice Quizzes

Quiz 3 Date: ...... / ...... / ......

1) True or false? The EM spectrum is continuous.
2) Give one example of a transverse wave.
3) What part of an atom can emit gamma rays?
4) Describe an experiment you could do to measure the speed of sound in air.
5) True or false? Waves transfer energy and matter.
6) What type of EM wave lies between radio waves and infrared on the EM spectrum?
7) State two uses of ultraviolet waves.
8) What is meant by the 'wavelength' of a wave?
9) Give two harmful effects of exposure to X-rays and gamma rays.
10) What is refraction?

Total:

Quiz 4 Date: ...... / ...... / ......

1) Give two harmful effects of exposure to ultraviolet radiation.
2) Define wave speed.
3) True or false? Ripples on a water's surface carry the water away.
4) What type of EM wave can be used in optical fibres?
5) True or false? EM waves transfer energy from absorber to source.
6) What is meant by the 'frequency' of a wave?
7) Describe the difference between transverse and longitudinal waves.
8) True or false? Changes in atoms and their nuclei cause EM waves to be created or absorbed over a large frequency range.
9) What does radiation dose measure?
10) Between radio waves and gamma rays, which has:
    a) the lowest frequency? b) the shortest wavelength?

Total:

Magnets

Magnetic Fields

PERMANENT MAGNET — [   ]

Magnetic field is [   ] at the poles.

Magnetic field strength [   ] with distance from magnet.

Field lines show [   ] force would act on a [   ], if placed at that point.

MAGNETIC FIELD — region where [   ] [   ] experience a force.

Field is [   ] where field lines are closer together.

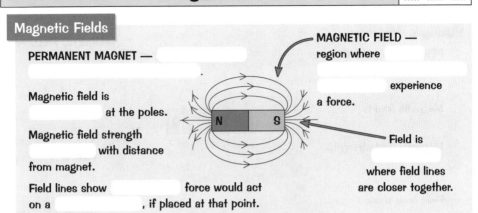

Repulsion

.... poles repel.

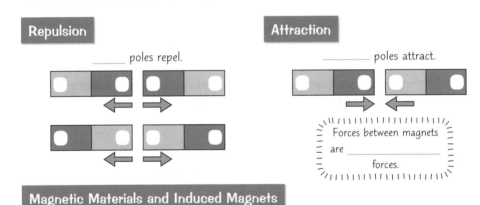

Attraction

.... poles attract.

Forces between magnets are .... forces.

Magnetic Materials and Induced Magnets

INDUCED MAGNET — a [   ] that turns into a magnet when it's put in [   ].

Four magnetic materials:

1. iron
2. [   ]
3. nickel
4. [   ]

permanent magnet   induced magnet

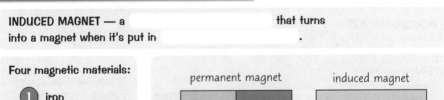

A permanent magnet and an induced magnet are always [   ] to each other.

When the induced magnet is moved away from the permanent magnet, it [   ]

Magnets

Second Go:
..... /..... /.....

Magnetic Fields

PERMANENT MAGNET —

Magnetic field is

Magnetic field strength

Field lines show

MAGNETIC FIELD —

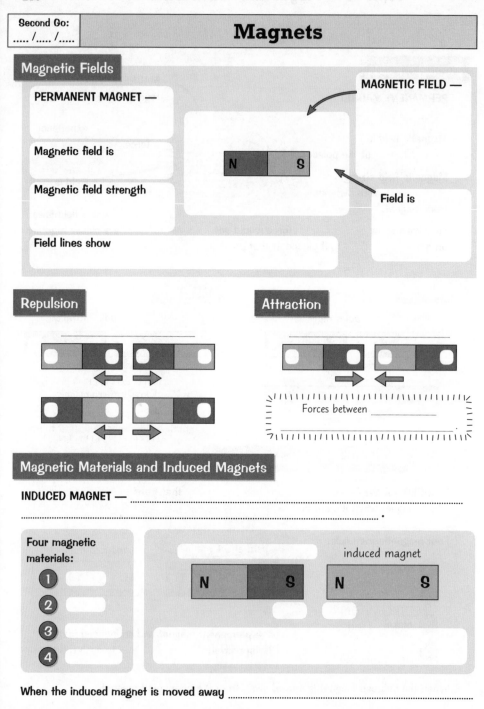

Field is

Repulsion

Attraction

Forces between _____

Magnetic Materials and Induced Magnets

INDUCED MAGNET — ....

....

Four magnetic materials:

1. _____
2. _____
3. _____
4. _____

induced magnet

When the induced magnet is moved away ....

....

Compasses and Electromagnetism

Compasses

Compass needle points in the direction of

[ ].

A compass needle is

[ ].

When a compass isn't near a magnet, its needle points [ ] to line up with the Earth's [ ].

Current-Carrying Wire

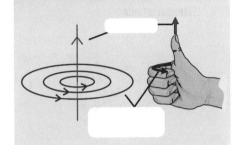

Two factors the magnetic field strength depends on:

1 Size of [ ].

2 [ ] the wire.

Solenoids and Magnetic Fields

Twisting a wire into a solenoid [ ] the magnetic field strength around the wire.

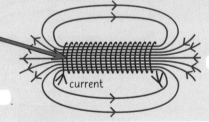

Magnetic fields of each turn of wire [ ].

So magnetic field inside solenoid is [ ].

current

magnetic field (same shape as a [ ])

ELECTROMAGNET — a solenoid with an [ ]. It is a [ ] magnet that can be [ ].

Putting an [ ] [ ] increases [ ].

Topic P7 — Magnetism and Electromagnetism

Compasses and Electromagnetism

Compasses

Compass needle

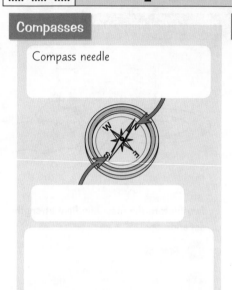

Current-Carrying Wire

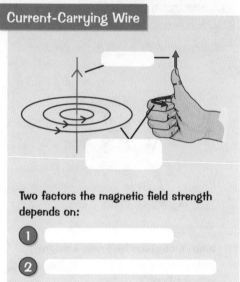

Two factors the magnetic field strength depends on:

1

2

Solenoids and Magnetic Fields

Twisting a wire into a solenoid ....
....

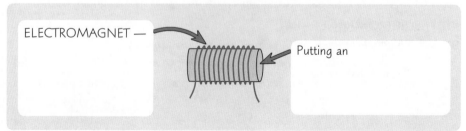

Magnetic fields of

So magnetic field

current

magnetic field

ELECTROMAGNET —

Putting an

Topic P7 — Magnetism and Electromagnetism

Mixed Practice Quizzes

If testing your knowledge sounds attractive, try the questions on p.269-272 below.

Quiz 1   Date: ...... / ...... / ......

1) True or false? A compass needle points in the direction of the magnetic field it's in.

2) What is an electromagnet?

3) True or false? An iron bar becomes an induced magnet in a magnetic field.

4) Where is the magnetic field of a bar magnet strongest?

5) Describe the magnetic field shape around a straight current-carrying wire.

6) True or false? A compass needle is a small electromagnet.

7) How does twisting a wire into a solenoid affect the magnetic field strength around the wire?

8) What is a permanent magnet?

9) Are the forces that act between magnets contact or non-contact forces?

10) What happens when two like poles are brought near each other?

Total:

Quiz 2   Date: ...... / ...... / ......

1) True or false? The strength of the magnetic field around a current-carrying wire depends on the direction of the current.

2) Which pole do magnetic field lines point away from?

3) What is a magnetic field?

4) Give one way to increase a solenoid's magnetic field strength.

5) True or false? A permanent magnet and an induced magnet are always attracted to each other.

6) What is a solenoid with an iron core called?

7) True or false? A steel bar would turn into a magnet in a magnetic field.

8) What is an induced magnet?

9) What happens when a north pole of one magnet and a south pole of another magnet are brought near to each other?

10) When a compass isn't near another magnet, does it point north or south?

Total:

Topic P7 — Magnetism and Electromagnetism

274

Mixed Practice Quizzes

Quiz 3 Date: ...... / ...... / ......

1) What two factors affect the magnetic field strength around a current-carrying wire?
2) True or false? A cobalt rod cannot become an induced magnet.
3) Describe the shape of the magnetic field outside a solenoid.
4) True or false? Magnetic forces are contact forces.
5) What happens when two magnetic north poles are brought near each other?
6) What type of magnet loses its magnetism when it's removed from a magnetic field?
7) Name two magnetic materials.
8) True or false? Field lines are closer together at points where the magnetic field is weaker.
9) Why does a compass needle point north when it's not near a magnet?
10) Describe the magnetic field inside a solenoid.

Total:

Quiz 4 Date: ...... / ...... / ......

1) Does a current-carrying wire produce a stronger magnetic field when it is straight or when it is twisted into a solenoid?
2) What does the direction of magnetic field lines show?
3) What happens when two unlike poles are brought near to each other?
4) True or false? A magnet experiences a force in a magnetic field.
5) How does adding an iron core to a solenoid affect its magnetic field?
6) What happens to the magnetic field of an induced magnet when it is removed from an external magnetic field?
7) Which pole do magnetic field lines point towards?
8) True or false? The magnetic field strength of a permanent magnet decreases with distance from the magnet.
9) What is a compass needle?
10) True or false? The magnetic field outside a solenoid is strong and uniform.

Total:

Biology Required Practicals 1

Microscopy

Start with the [____] lens then move the stage up with the [____] adjustment knob.

Look down the [____] and adjust the [____] with the adjustment knobs (use the coarse one first).

To see the slide with a greater [____], swap to a higher-powered lens and [____].

When drawing your observations:
- use a [____]
- draw [____] lines
- [____] important features
- include a [____].

Water drop

Eyepiece

Coarse adjustment knob

[____] lenses

Specimen stained with e.g. [____]

Slide

Stage light

Stage

[____] knob

Onion cells

nucleus

cell wall

cytoplasm

real length = 0.25 mm

magnification = × 100

Osmosis

Four steps to investigate the effect of [____] of sugar or salt solutions on plant tissue:

1 Cut a potato into [____] cylinders.

2 [____] of each cylinder.

3 Prepare beakers containing different concentrations of sugar or salt solution and one of [____]. Put one cylinder in each beaker.

4 Leave for 24 hours and then take out the cylinders and [____] [____]. Measure their masses again.

[____] or sugar/salt solution

Potato cylinder

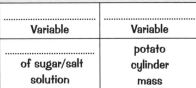

.... Variable	.... Variable
.... of sugar/salt solution	potato cylinder mass

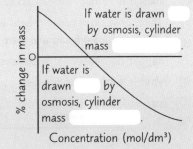

If water is drawn [____] by osmosis, cylinder mass [____].

If water is drawn [____] by osmosis, cylinder mass [____].

% change in mass

Concentration (mol/dm³)

$$\% \text{ change in mass} = \frac{\text{new mass} - \text{original mass}}{[\_\_\_\_]} \times [\_\_\_\_]$$

Biology Required Practicals 1

Microscopy

Start with the

Look down the

To see the

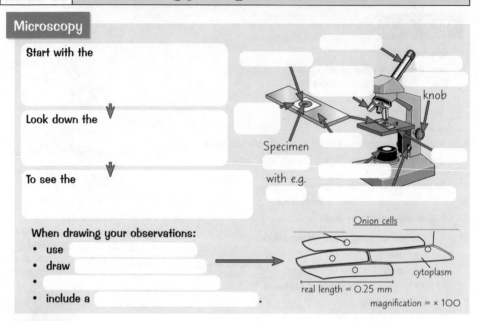

knob

Specimen

with e.g.

When drawing your observations:
- use
- draw
-
- include a

Onion cells

cytoplasm

real length = 0.25 mm

magnification = × 100

Osmosis

Four steps to investigate the effect of

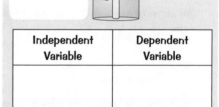

1. Cut a potato

2. Measure the

3. Prepare beakers containing different

4. Leave for 24 hours and then

Independent Variable	Dependent Variable

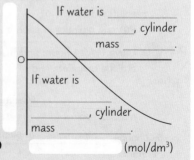

If water is _____ _____, cylinder mass _____.

O

If water is _____ _____, cylinder mass _____.

(mol/dm³)

$$= \frac{\text{mass} - \text{mass}}{} \times 100$$

 ✓ ✓ ✓

Biology Required Practicals 2

Effect of pH on Amylase Activity

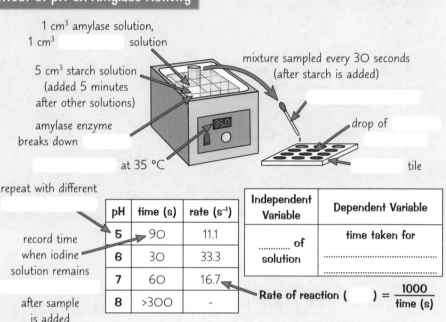

1 cm³ amylase solution,
1 cm³ ⬚⬚⬚⬚ solution

5 cm³ starch solution
(added 5 minutes
after other solutions)

amylase enzyme
breaks down ⬚⬚⬚⬚

⬚⬚⬚⬚ at 35 °C

mixture sampled every 30 seconds
(after starch is added)

drop of ⬚⬚⬚⬚

⬚⬚⬚⬚ tile

repeat with different ⬚⬚⬚⬚

record time
when iodine
solution remains
⬚⬚⬚⬚
after sample
is added

pH	time (s)	rate (s⁻¹)
5	90	11.1
6	30	33.3
7	60	16.7
8	>300	–

Independent Variable	Dependent Variable
.... of solution	time taken for ....

$$\text{Rate of reaction } (\quad) = \frac{1000}{\text{time (s)}}$$

Food Tests

Test	Method	Positive result
Benedict's test (for ....)	Add about .... drops of Benedict's solution to a 5 cm³ food sample and leave for 5 minutes at .... °C.	.... → .... yellow brick red
.... test (for starch)	Add a few drops of .... solution to a 5 cm³ food sample and mix.	.... - .... → blue-black
Biuret test (for ....)	Add 2 cm³ of biuret solution to a 2 cm³ food sample and mix.	blue → ....
.... test (for ....)	Add 3 drops of .... stain solution to a 5 cm³ food sample and mix.	Mixture separates into two layers — ....

 ☑ ☑ 😊 ☑

Biology Required Practicals 2

Effect of pH on Amylase Activity

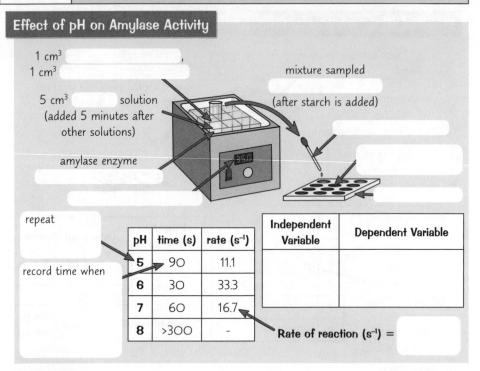

1 cm³ _____,
1 cm³ _____

5 cm³ _____ solution
(added 5 minutes after
other solutions)

amylase enzyme

mixture sampled
(after starch is added)

repeat _____

record time when _____

pH	time (s)	rate (s⁻¹)
5	90	11.1
6	30	33.3
7	60	16.7
8	>300	-

Independent Variable	Dependent Variable

Rate of reaction (s⁻¹) = _____

Food Tests

Test	Method	Positive result
_____ test (for _____)	Add about 10 drops of Benedict's solution to a 5 cm³ food sample and _____	blue
_____ (for starch)		
Biuret test (for _____)	Add _____ to a 2 cm³ food sample and mix.	
	Add _____ of Sudan III stain solution to a 5 cm³ food sample and mix.	

Required Practicals

Biology Required Practicals 3

Effect of Light Intensity on Photosynthesis Rate

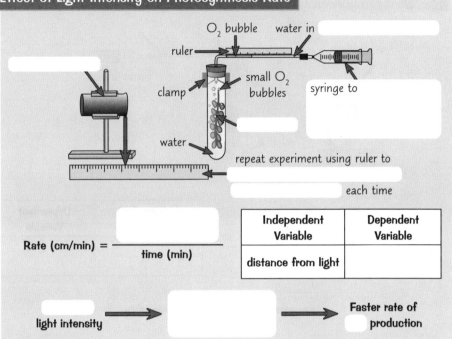

$$\text{Rate (cm/min)} = \frac{\boxed{}}{\text{time (min)}}$$

Independent Variable	Dependent Variable
distance from light	

light intensity ⟶ ⟶ Faster rate of production

Reaction Time

REACTION TIME —

Four steps to investigate reaction time:

1. Hold a ____ between the thumb and forefinger of the person being tested.

2. Drop the ruler without warning and ____.

3. ____ then calculate the mean distance that the ruler fell.

4. Repeat the experiment to investigate the effect of a factor on reaction time.

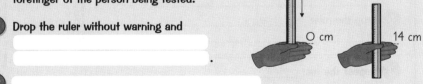

30 cm

0 cm   14 cm

The ____ the ruler falls, the ____ the reaction time.

 ☑ ☑ ☑

Biology Required Practicals 3

Effect of Light Intensity on Photosynthesis Rate

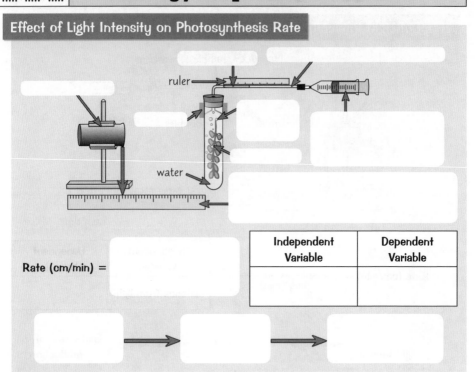

ruler

water

Rate (cm/min) =

Independent Variable	Dependent Variable

Reaction Time

REACTION TIME —

Four steps to investigate reaction time:

1 Hold a ruler ....
....
....

2 Drop the ruler ....
....
....

3 Repeat the test ....
....
....

4 Repeat the experiment ....
....
....

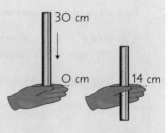

30 cm

O cm   14 cm

Biology Required Practicals 4

Distribution and Abundance of Organisms

Four steps to estimate population size of small organisms using [_____] :

1 Place a 1 m² [_____] at random in a field.

2 [_____] all the daisies within it.

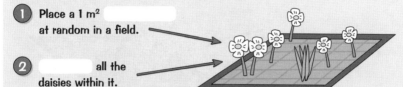

3 Repeat several times and work out the [_____]
[_____].

[_____] = $\dfrac{\text{total number of organisms}}{\text{_____}}$

4 Multiply the [_____] by the number of [_____].

Three steps to find how organisms are distributed across an area using [_____]
— e.g. distribution of daisies as you move away from the edge of a pond:

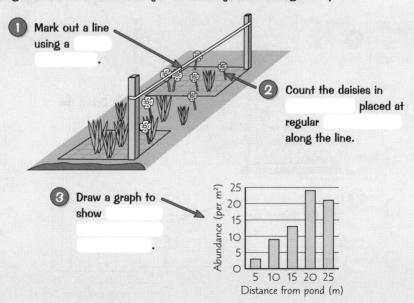

1 Mark out a line using a [_____].

2 Count the daisies in [_____] placed at regular [_____] along the line.

3 Draw a graph to show [_____]
[_____].

Abundance (per m²) vs Distance from pond (m)

Second Go:
..... /..... /.....

Biology Required Practicals 4

Distribution and Abundance of Organisms

Four steps to estimate [   ] of small organisms using [   ] :

1 [   ]

2 [   ]

3 [   ]

mean = [   ]

4 [   ]

Three steps to find how organisms are [   ] using
[   ] — e.g. distribution of daisies as you move away from the edge of a pond:

1 [   ]

2 Count the [   ]

3 Draw a graph to show
how the daisies are
[   ].

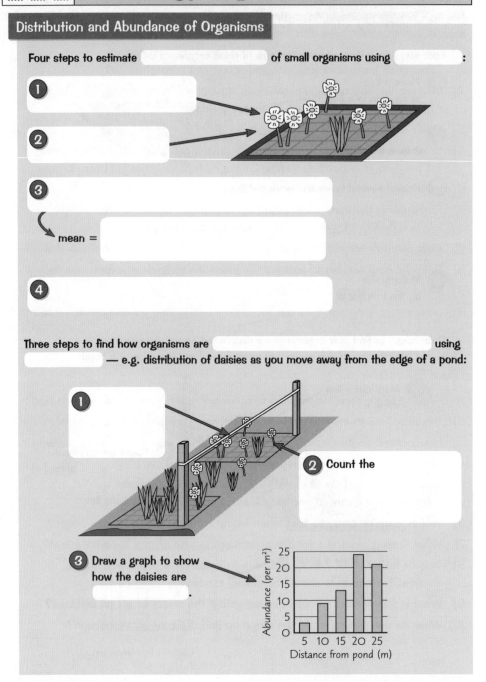

Abundance (per m²) vs Distance from pond (m)

Mixed Practice Quizzes

It's less fun than actually doing the practicals, but it's quiz-time for pages 275-282.

Quiz 1 | Date: ...... / ...... / ......

1) What does the coarse adjustment knob on a microscope do?

2) What is the dependent variable in an experiment investigating the effect of light intensity on the rate of photosynthesis?

3) What is meant by 'reaction time'?

4) What is the independent variable when investigating how the time taken for amylase to break down starch changes with different pH buffers?

5) Which food molecule is biuret solution used to test for?

6) Explain why the mass of a potato cylinder might decrease after being left in a beaker of salt solution for 24 hours.

7) How can you vary light intensity to investigate its effect on photosynthesis?

8) Describe how you could test for the presence of lipids in a food sample.

9) What are transects used to study?

10) What might a syringe be used for when investigating photosynthesis rate?

Total:

Quiz 2 | Date: ...... / ...... / ......

1) After testing a person's reaction time several times, what should you do next?

2) Describe how to investigate the distribution of a plant along a transect.

3) How can pH be controlled when investigating its effect on amylase activity?

4) How could you tell if starch was present in a food sample?

5) Describe how you could investigate the effect of light intensity on the rate of photosynthesis in pondweed.

6) Which knob do you use first when trying to focus a microscope image?

7) What does it mean if a food sample turns yellow after a Benedict's test?

8) True or false? When using quadrats to investigate population size in an area, the quadrats should be placed randomly.

9) What is iodine used for when investigating the effect of pH on amylase?

10) What do you use to move the stage up and down on a microscope?

Total:

Required Practicals

Mixed Practice Quizzes

Quiz 3   Date: ...... / ...... / ......

1) If sugar is not present in a food sample, what will the sample look like following the Benedict's test?

2) List four things you should do when drawing a microscope image of cells.

3) In an investigation into osmosis, what should be done to potato cylinders removed from salt solution, before they are weighed?

4) How would you calculate the % change in mass of a potato cylinder?

5) Describe how you could estimate the population size of a small organism in an area using quadrats.

6) How can you tell when amylase has broken down all the starch in a solution?

7) Describe how you could test for the presence of proteins in a food sample.

8) True or false? When using a microscope, use the lowest-powered lens first.

9) What is the dependent variable when investigating how the time taken for amylase to break down starch changes with different pH buffers?

10) What gas should you collect when investigating photosynthesis rate?

Total:

Quiz 4   Date: ...... / ...... / ......

1) A positive result of which food test involves a colour change to purple?

2) What is the independent variable in an experiment investigating the effect of light intensity on the rate of photosynthesis?

3) Describe how you could investigate a person's reaction time using a ruler.

4) How do you work out the rate at which amylase breaks down starch in s^{-1}?

5) When studying abundance, what's the next step after putting a quadrat down?

6) When studying osmosis, when do you measure a potato cylinder's mass?

7) What is a dropping pipette used for when investigating amylase activity?

8) Give two possible uses of a ruler when investigating the effect of light intensity on the rate of photosynthesis.

9) True or false? Calculating a mean isn't part of estimating population size.

10) When using a microscope, what goes between the slide and the coverslip?

Total:

Chemistry Required Practicals 1

Making Soluble Salts

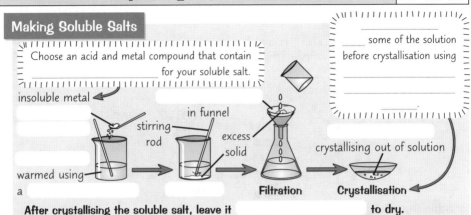

Choose an acid and metal compound that contain _____ for your soluble salt.

insoluble metal

stirring rod

in funnel

excess solid

warmed using

a _____

Filtration

_____ some of the solution before crystallisation using _____ .

crystallising out of solution

Crystallisation

After crystallising the soluble salt, leave it _____ to dry.

Electrolysis

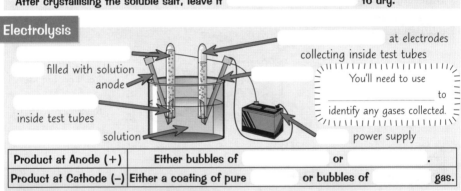

_____ at electrodes collecting inside test tubes

filled with solution

anode

inside test tubes

solution

You'll need to use _____ to identify any gases collected.

power supply

Product at Anode (+)	Either bubbles of _____ or _____ .
Product at Cathode (−)	Either a coating of pure _____ or bubbles of _____ gas.

Investigating Temperature Changes

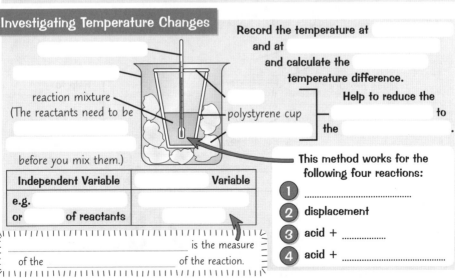

Record the temperature at _____ and at _____ and calculate the temperature difference.

reaction mixture
(The reactants need to be _____ before you mix them.)

polystyrene cup

Help to reduce the _____ to the _____ .

This method works for the following four reactions:

1. ....
2. displacement
3. acid + ...
4. acid + ...

Independent Variable	_____ Variable
e.g. _____	
or _____ of reactants	

_____ is the measure of the _____ of the reaction.

Required Practicals

Chemistry Required Practicals 1

Making Soluble Salts

Choose an acid and metal compound that ....
....

....
.... before
crystallisation ....
....
....

filter
paper in

Mixing   **Filtration**

After crystallising ....

Electrolysis

cathode

power supply

You'll need to use
....
to identify ....

Product at	Either
Product at	Either

Investigating Temperature Changes

Record the temperature

reaction mixture

Help to

This method works for the following four reactions:

1 ....
2 ....
3 .... + ...
4 .... +
....

e.g.

is the measure of

Chemistry Required Practicals 2

Two Ways of Measuring Rates of Reaction

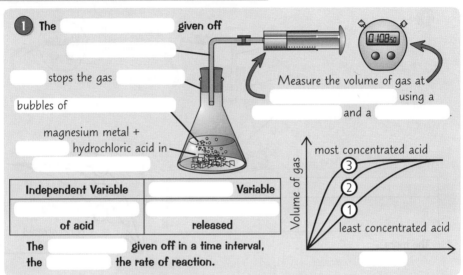

1 The _____ given off _____

_____ stops the gas _____

bubbles of _____

magnesium metal + _____ hydrochloric acid in _____

Measure the volume of gas at _____ using a _____ and a _____

most concentrated acid

least concentrated acid

Volume of gas

3
2
1

Independent Variable	_____ Variable
_____ of acid	_____ released

The _____ given off in a time interval, the _____ the rate of reaction.

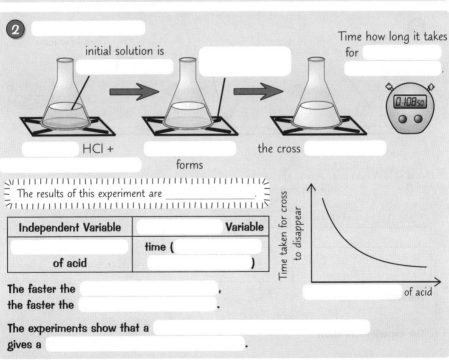

2 _____

initial solution is _____

Time how long it takes for _____

HCl + _____ _____ forms

the cross _____

The results of this experiment are _____ .

Independent Variable	_____ Variable
_____ of acid	time (_____)

Time taken for cross to disappear

_____ of acid

The faster the _____ , the faster the _____

The experiments show that a _____ gives a _____ .

Chemistry Required Practicals 2

Two Ways of Measuring Rates of Reaction

1

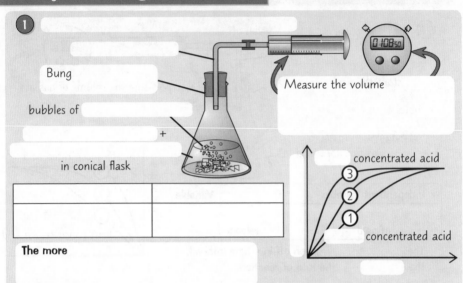

Bung

bubbles of

+

in conical flask

Measure the volume

The more

concentrated acid

③
②
①

concentrated acid

2

initial solution

Time how long

The _____ of this experiment _____.

The faster

The experiments show

Chemistry Required Practicals 3

Paper Chromatography

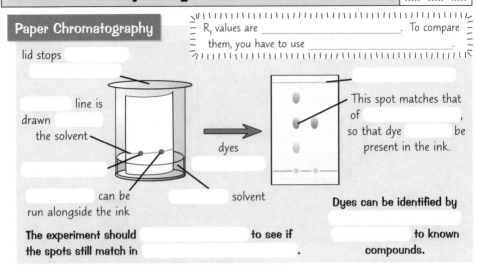

R$_f$ values are _____ . To compare them, you have to use _____ .

lid stops [____]

[____] line is drawn

the solvent

[____] can be run alongside the ink

dyes

[____] solvent

This spot matches that of [____], so that dye [____] be present in the ink.

[____]

Dyes can be identified by _____ to known compounds.

The experiment should [____] to see if the spots still match in [____].

Five Steps for the Purification of Water

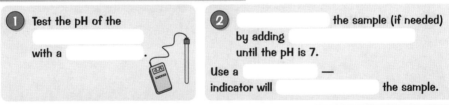

1 Test the pH of the [____] with a [____].

2 [____] the sample (if needed) by adding [____] until the pH is 7.

Use a [____] — indicator will [____] the sample.

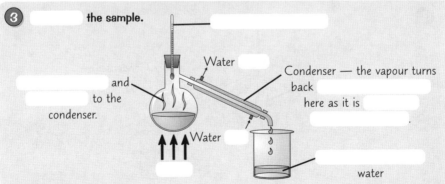

3 [____] the sample.

[____]

[____] and [____] to the condenser.

Water [____]

Water [____]

Condenser — the vapour turns back [____] here as it is [____].

[____] water

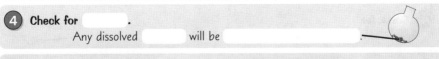

4 Check for [____].

Any dissolved [____] will be [____].

5 [____] the pH of the [____] water to check it's [____].

Required Practicals

Chemistry Required Practicals 3

Paper Chromatography

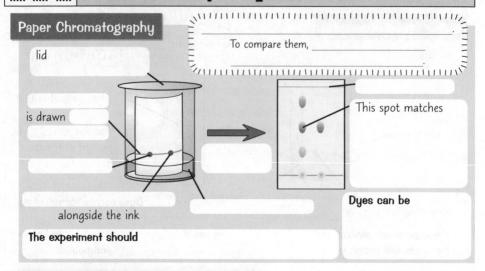

lid

_____
To compare them, _____
_____

is drawn

This spot matches

alongside the ink

Dyes can be

The experiment should

Five Steps for the Purification of Water

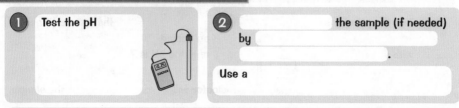

1 Test the pH

2 _____ the sample (if needed)
by _____
_____ .

Use a

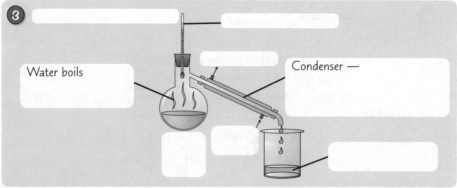

3 _____

Water boils

Condenser —

4 Check for _____ .
Any dissolved _____ .

5 Retest the pH

Mixed Practice Quizzes

Feeling practical after p.285-290? Don't worry — you won't have to build any flat-pack furniture or anything like that. Just see how you get on with these quizzes.

Quiz 1　　Date: ...... / ...... / ......

1) How can you measure the volume of gas produced in a reaction?
2) Why is a pH meter used to measure pH during water purification?
3) What type of power supply is used for electrolysis?
4) Where should the pencil line in chromatography be relative to the solvent?
5) Why is cotton wool often used in experiments measuring temperature change?
6) True or false? Temperature change can be used to measure energy change.
7) How does distillation separate water from dissolved salts?
8) True or false? When making a soluble salt from an insoluble metal compound, the excess solid is removed by evaporation.
9) Why might chemical tests be used in an electrolysis experiment?
10) What could you use to measure time in a rate of reaction experiment?

Total:

Quiz 2　　Date: ...... / ...... / ......

1) True or false? The concentration of reactants could be the independent variable when investigating the temperature change of a reaction.
2) Give one limitation of the method for measuring the rate of precipitation formation where a cross is observed through a reaction vessel.
3) What should be considered when choosing an insoluble metal compound for making a particular soluble salt?
4) Give an example of a product that could form at the anode in electrolysis.
5) How could you dry the solid product of crystallisation?
6) Describe how to neutralise a sample of impure water.
7) Describe one test performed after the distillation step in water purification.
8) What name is given to a solution that is undergoing electrolysis?
9) Give two possible dependent variables for measuring the rate of a reaction.
10) True or false? Add the insoluble compound to cold acid to make a soluble salt.

Total:

Mixed Practice Quizzes

Date: ...... / ...... / ......

1) Describe how to remove excess solid from a solution by filtration. ☑

2) What can you say about the rate of a reaction compared to another if it produces more gas in the same time period? ☑

3) Describe how to collect the gaseous products of electrolysis. ☑

4) How could you confirm the presence of a certain dye in a mixture if it matches the spot from a pure dye in a chromatogram? ☑

5) Give two types of insoluble metal compound used to make soluble salts. ☑

6) Describe how to measure the temperature change of a reaction mixture. ☑

7) What should you use to measure the pH of water during water purification? ☑

8) Suggest three ways to minimise energy loss from a reaction mixture. ☑

9) What should you use to draw the baseline on chromatography paper? ☑

10) What is the role of the condenser during the distillation of water? ☑

Total:

Quiz 4 Date: ...... / ...... / ......

1) Give two types of reaction suitable for a temperature change investigation. ☑

2) True or false? When using a condenser, the cold water should go in at the bottom and flow out of the top of the condenser. ☑

3) When making soluble salts, which step follows the filtration step? ☑

4) How does increasing the concentration of hydrochloric acid (HCl) affect the rate of its reaction with sodium thiosulfate? ☑

5) Why might a lid be used in a chromatography experiment? ☑

6) Give two examples of products that can form at the cathode in electrolysis. ☑

7) Give an example of a reaction whose rate could be investigated by measuring the volume of gas produced over time. ☑

8) Following neutralisation, what should the pH of a sample of water be? ☑

9) Which is the negative electrode in an electrolysis experiment? ☑

10) True or false? R_f values can only be compared if the same solvent has been used. ☑

Total:

Physics Required Practicals 1

Specific Heat Capacity

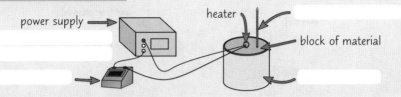

power supply ⟶

heater

block of material

Six steps to find specific heat capacity of material:

1 Turn on [_____].

2 Measure [_____] every minute for [_____].

3 Calculate power with [_____].

4 For each minute over the [_____], calculate [_____] with [_____] (*t* is time in seconds).

5 [_____] ⟶

6 Specific heat capacity = [_____]

Temperature / °C

Energy transferred / J

Investigating How Length of Wire Affects Resistance

- Change length of wire by moving [_____].

- For each length, [_____] with [_____].

Keep wire at a _____ _____ throughout experiment.

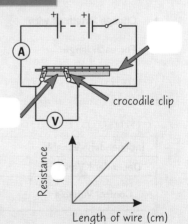

crocodile clip

Independent Variable	
Dependent Variable	
Control Variable	

Resistance ( )

Length of wire (cm)

Physics Required Practicals 1

Specific Heat Capacity

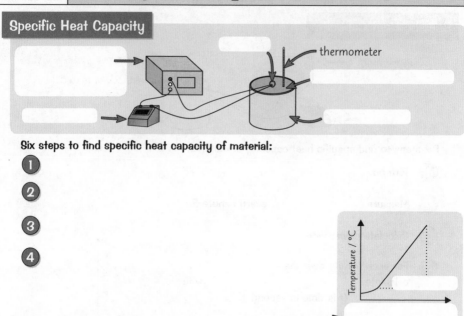

thermometer

Six steps to find specific heat capacity of material:

①

②

③

④

⑤ Plot graph.

⑥

Investigating How Length of Wire Affects Resistance

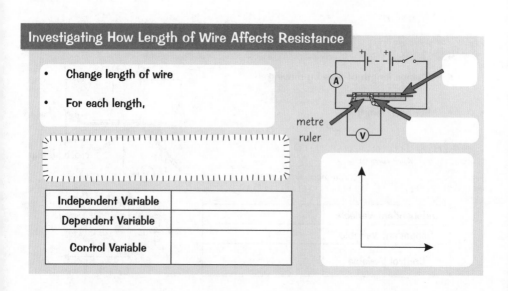

• Change length of wire

• For each length,

metre ruler

Independent Variable	
Dependent Variable	
Control Variable	

Physics Required Practicals 2

Investigating Resistance in Series and Parallel Circuits

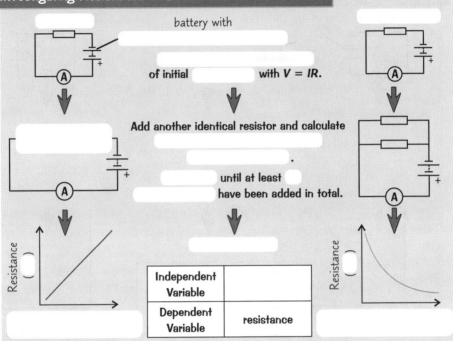

battery with

of initial _____ with **V = IR.**

Add another identical resistor and calculate

_____ until at least _____ have been added in total.

Resistance

Resistance

Independent Variable	
Dependent Variable	resistance

I-V Characteristics

Three steps to find a component's I-V characteristic:

1 Vary _____ to change _____ through circuit, and then take a reading of _____.

_____

2 _____ connected to battery (so current is _____) and repeat _____.

3 Plot values on _____.

component

Resistor (at constant temperature)

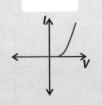

Physics Required Practicals 2

Investigating Resistance in Series and Parallel Circuits

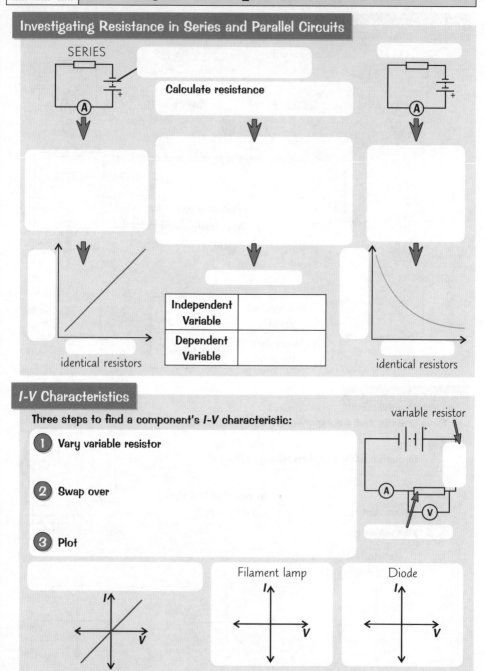

SERIES

Calculate resistance

Independent Variable	
Dependent Variable	

identical resistors

identical resistors

I-V Characteristics

Three steps to find a component's I-V characteristic:

1 Vary variable resistor

2 Swap over

3 Plot

variable resistor

Filament lamp

Diode

Required Practicals

Physics Required Practicals 3

Determining Density of Solids and Liquids

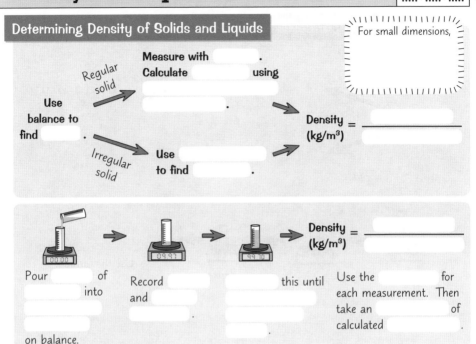

For small dimensions,

Use balance to find _____.

Regular solid →

Measure with _____.
Calculate _____ using _____.

Irregular solid → Use _____ to find _____.

Density = _____
(kg/m³)

Pour _____ of _____ into _____ on balance.

Record _____ and _____.

this until

Use the _____ for each measurement. Then take an _____ of calculated _____.

Density = _____
(kg/m³)

Investigating Springs

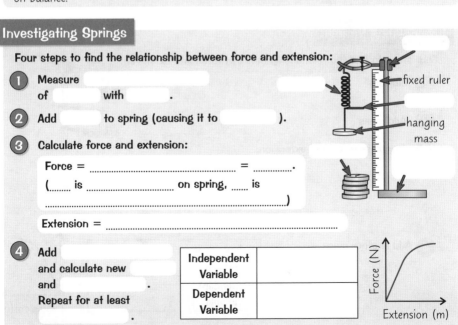

Four steps to find the relationship between force and extension:

1 Measure _____ of _____ with _____.

2 Add _____ to spring (causing it to _____).

3 Calculate force and extension:

Force = ... = ...

(........ is .... on spring, ... is

....)

Extension = ...

4 Add _____ and calculate new _____ and _____.
Repeat for at least _____.

fixed ruler

hanging mass

Independent Variable	
Dependent Variable	

Physics Required Practicals 3

Determining Density of Solids and Liquids

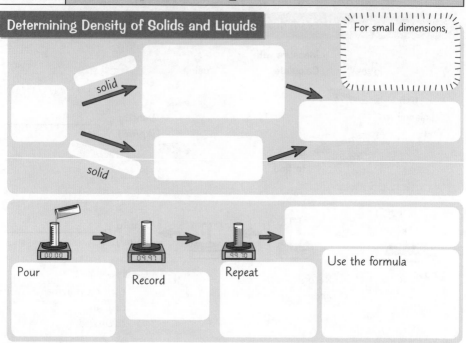

For small dimensions,

Pour

Record

Repeat

Use the formula

Investigating Springs

Four steps to find the relationship between force and extension:

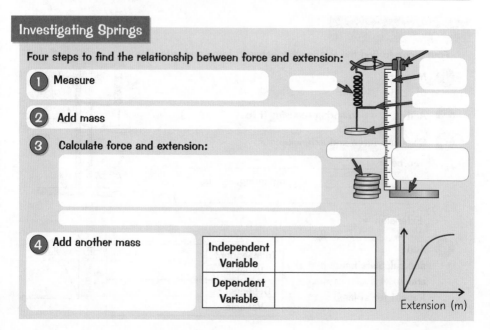

1 Measure

2 Add mass

3 Calculate force and extension:

4 Add another mass

| Independent Variable | |
| Dependent Variable | |

Extension (m)

Physics Required Practicals 4

Two Experiments that Test $F = ma$

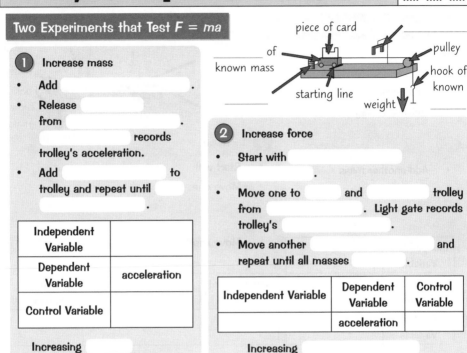

1 Increase mass

- Add [_____].
- Release from [_____].
- [_____] records trolley's acceleration.
- Add [_____] to trolley and repeat until [_____].

piece of card

[_____] of known mass

pulley

starting line

hook of known weight

Independent Variable	
Dependent Variable	acceleration
Control Variable	

Increasing [_____] [_____] acceleration.

2 Increase force

- Start with [_____].
- Move one to [_____] and [_____] trolley from [_____]. Light gate records trolley's [_____].
- Move another [_____] and repeat until all masses [_____].

Independent Variable	Dependent Variable	Control Variable
	acceleration	

Increasing [_____] increases acceleration.

Investigating IR Radiation

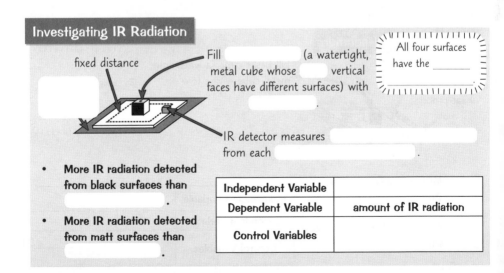

fixed distance

Fill [_____] (a watertight, metal cube whose [_____] vertical faces have different surfaces) with [_____].

All four surfaces have the [_____].

IR detector measures [_____] from each [_____].

- More IR radiation detected from black surfaces than [_____].
- More IR radiation detected from matt surfaces than [_____].

Independent Variable	
Dependent Variable	amount of IR radiation
Control Variables	

Physics Required Practicals 4

Two Experiments that Test $F = ma$

1 Increase [ ]

- **Add mass**
- **Release trolley**

- **Add another mass**

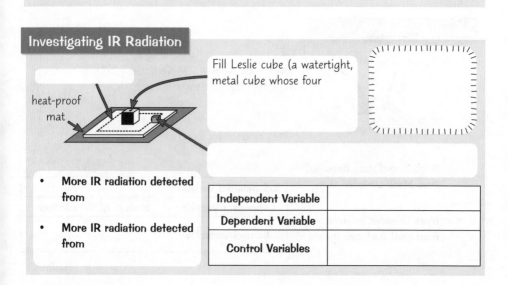

pulley

hook of known mass

starting line

2 Increase [ ]

- **Start with**
- **Move one**

- **Move another**

Independent Variable	
Dependent Variable	
Control Variable	

Increasing [ ]

Independent Variable	Dependent Variable	Control Variable

Increasing [ ]

Investigating IR Radiation

heat-proof mat

Fill Leslie cube (a watertight, metal cube whose four

- **More IR radiation detected from**

- **More IR radiation detected from**

Independent Variable	
Dependent Variable	
Control Variables	

Physics Required Practicals 5

Two Ways to Measure Wave Speed

1 Waves in a ripple tank.

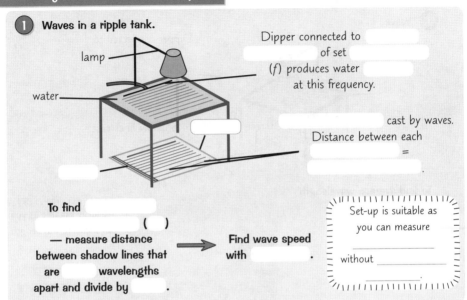

lamp

water

Dipper connected to [ ]
of set [ ]
(*f*) produces water [ ]
at this frequency.

[ ] cast by waves.
Distance between each
[ ] =
.

To find [ ]
[ ] **( )**
— measure distance
between shadow lines that
are [ ] wavelengths
apart and divide by [ ].

→ **Find wave speed
with** [ ].

Set-up is suitable as
you can measure
....
without ....
.

2 Waves in a solid.

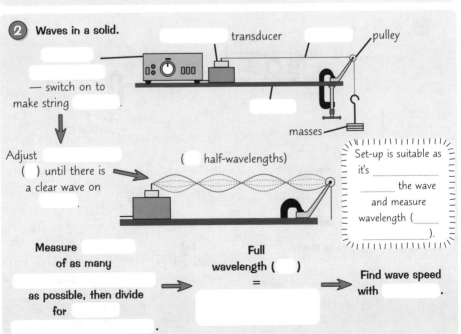

transducer [ ]   pulley

[ ]

— switch on to
make string [ ].

masses

Adjust [ ]
( ) until there is
a clear wave on
[ ].

([ ] half-wavelengths)

Set-up is suitable as
it's ....
.... the wave
and measure
wavelength (............
...............).

Measure [ ]
of as many
[ ]
as possible, then divide
for [ ]
[ ].

**Full
wavelength ( )**
=
[ ]

→ **Find wave speed
with** [ ].

Physics Required Practicals 5

Two Ways to Measure Wave Speed

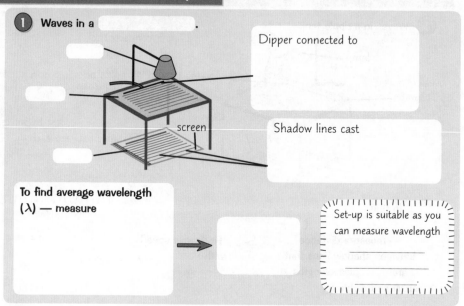

1 Waves in a [_____].

Dipper connected to

[_____]

[_____]

screen

Shadow lines cast

[_____]

To find average wavelength (λ) — measure

Set-up is suitable as you can measure wavelength
....
....
....

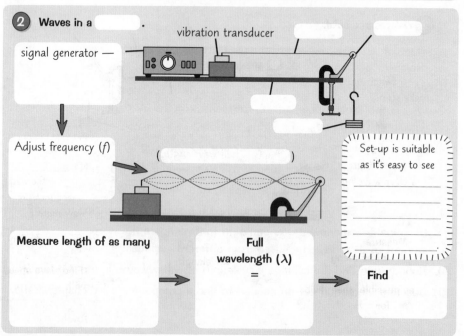

2 Waves in a [_____].

signal generator —

vibration transducer

[_____]

[_____]

Adjust frequency (f)

(   )

Set-up is suitable as it's easy to see
....
....
....
....

Measure length of as many

Full wavelength (λ) =

Find

Mixed Practice Quizzes

Phew, what a lot of practicals. Here are some quizzes for you testing p.293-302.

Quiz 1 | Date: ...... / ...... / ......

1) Describe an experiment to measure the wave speed on a piece of string.
2) What shape is the *I-V* graph for a filament lamp?
3) What piece of apparatus can be used to measure a trolley's acceleration?
4) How can you measure the volume of an irregular solid?
5) Does the total resistance of a circuit increase or decrease when you add resistors in: a) series? b) parallel?
6) Describe how to find the specific heat capacity of a material.
7) In the trolley experiment that tests $F = ma$, what provides the force?
8) Name five pieces of apparatus needed to investigate the relationship between force and extension in springs.
9) True or false? All the surfaces of a Leslie cube have different temperatures.
10) Describe how to set up an experiment to investigate how the resistance of a wire changes with length.

Total:

Quiz 2 | Date: ...... / ...... / ......

1) How can you use a graph of temperature against energy transferred (from the specific heat capacity experiment) to calculate specific heat capacity?
2) What is a Leslie cube?
3) Why is the experimental set-up for measuring the wavelength of a wave on a string suitable?
4) How does the resistance of a wire vary with its length?
5) List the apparatus needed for the trolley experiments that test $F = ma$.
6) Describe how to determine the density of a liquid.
7) How do you calculate the force acting on a spring with hanging masses?
8) Describe an experiment you could do to investigate the amount of IR radiation emitted from different surfaces.
9) How do you find the average wavelength of water waves in a ripple tank?
10) Describe the circuit set-up needed to find a component's *I-V* characteristic.

Total:

Mixed Practice Quizzes

Quiz 3   Date: ...... / ...... / ......

1) In an experiment investigating the relationship between the length of a wire and its resistance, what would the independent variable be? ☑

2) True or false? Light gates are used to find a component's *I-V* characteristic. ☑

3) Name two pieces of apparatus used for measuring small dimensions. ☑

4) Why is the experimental set-up for measuring the wavelength of water waves in a ripple tank suitable? ☑

5) How do you calculate the extension of a spring from its natural length? ☑

6) When using a trolley to test how increasing the force applied affects acceleration, what is the control variable? ☑

7) How can you determine the density of a regular solid? ☑

8) Describe an experiment you could do to investigate how the resistance in a circuit is affected by adding identical resistors in series. ☑

9) Name a piece of safety apparatus that should be used with a Leslie cube. ☑

10) Describe the experimental set-up to find a material's specific heat capacity. ☑

Total: [   ]

Quiz 4   Date: ...... / ...... / ......

1) True or false? When investigating how the resistance of a wire varies with its length, the temperature of the wire should be kept constant. ☑

2) Describe an experiment to find the force-extension relationship of a spring. ☑

3) State two control variables in the experiment for investigating IR radiation. ☑

4) List the apparatus needed in an experiment to find the density of a liquid. ☑

5) Describe an experiment to find a component's *I-V* characteristic. ☑

6) Describe how to measure the speed of water waves in a ripple tank. ☑

7) Give the independent variable in an experiment that investigates how the total resistance of a circuit changes when adding resistors in parallel. ☑

8) What two values should be plotted on a graph in the specific heat capacity experiment to determine the specific heat capacity of a material? ☑

9) Name an electrical component used to vary the current through a circuit. ☑

10) Describe two experiments you can do to test $F = ma$. ☑

Total: [   ]

Required Practicals

Measuring 1

Measuring Mass

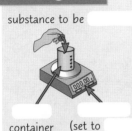

substance to be

container   (set to   )

Transferring solid to   :

When making a solution,   remaining solid
out of the   with
the   .

or

Find the   of the
container and   before and
after you   .

Three Ways to Measure Liquids

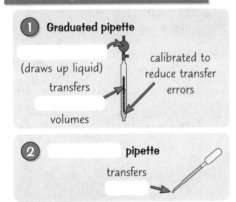

1 Graduated pipette

(draws up liquid)
transfers

volumes

calibrated to
reduce transfer
errors

2   pipette

transfers

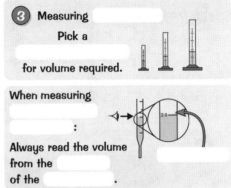

3 Measuring

Pick a

for volume required.

When measuring

                :

Always read the volume
from the
of the   .

Measuring Time

are

the timer
at   right time

Measuring Temperature

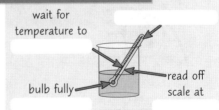

wait for
temperature to

bulb fully

read off
scale at

Measuring the Volume of a Solid

fill
with water to just

put the object in
and
             in a
measuring cylinder

object's volume
=

Practical Skills

Measuring 1

Measuring Mass

solid to   :

When making a solution,

or

Find the difference

Three Ways to Measure Liquids

1 **Graduated pipette**

calibrated to

transfers

2

3

Pick a

When

Always read

Measuring Time

Measuring Temperature

wait for

bulb

Measuring the Volume of a Solid

put the object in and

=

Practical Skills

Measuring 2

Measuring Length

ruler should be ⬚

to object

take reading
at ⬚

⬚ can measure small distances accurately.

use a ⬚
to make sure you
always ⬚

⬚

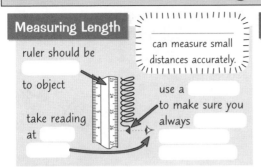

Measuring Angles

align angle vertex
with ⬚

measure the
angle ⬚

⬚

line up ⬚
with one angle line

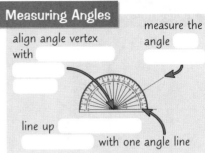

Measuring pH

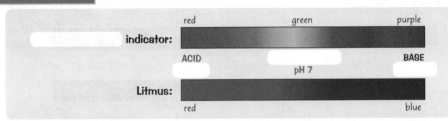

⬚ indicator:

red   green   purple

ACID   ⬚   BASE
pH 7

Litmus:

red   blue

Indicator solution	Indicator ⬚
Changes colour of ⬚	• For testing ⬚ of solution
	• Use ⬚ to test gases

pH probes and ⬚
give a ⬚ value for pH.

⬚

Measuring the Volume of Gases

⬚

system ⬚ with a
⬚ so no gas escapes

⬚ tube

⬚ gas
an ⬚
⬚ of water

⬚
filled and
⬚ in a beaker of water

Using a gas syringe is
⬚ than this
— some gases ⬚
⬚ which affects the
amount in the ⬚
⬚.

Amount of gas collected is ⬚
between the ⬚ volumes
in the ⬚.

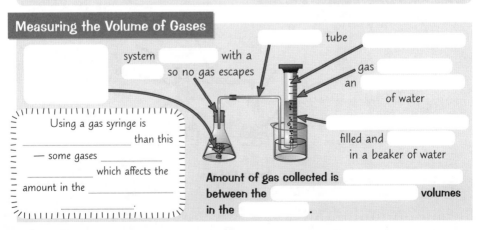

Practical Skills

Measuring 2

Measuring Length

Micrometers

ruler should be

use a

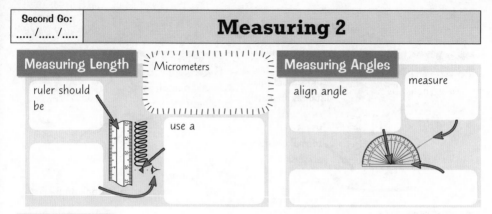

Measuring Angles

align angle

measure

Measuring pH

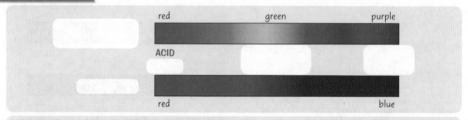

red   green   purple

ACID

red   blue

Indicator solution	
Changes	• For testing • Use

pH probes and

Measuring the Volume of Gases

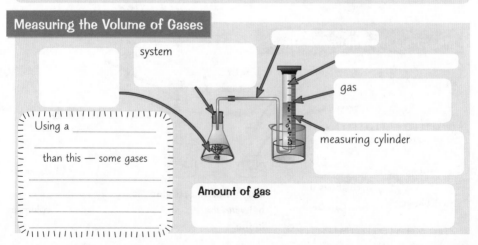

system

gas

Using a ....
.... than this — some gases

measuring cylinder

Amount of gas

Safety and Heating Substances

Safety Precautions

Read [____] before starting an experiment, and [____] throughout.

Use a [____] when [____] to avoid spillages.

Use a fume cupboard to avoid [____] like chlorine.

Wear safety goggles, [____] and [____] to protect against [____] or [____] chemicals.

Work in a [____] area.

Use clamp stands to stop [____]

Don't handle [____] directly.

When [____] a liquid, add the [____] substance to the [____].

Use a [____] to transfer solids.

Keep [____] away from [____].

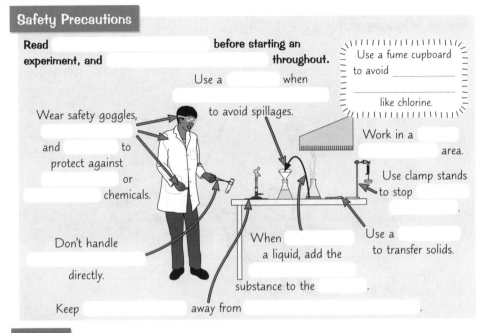

Heating

Bunsen burners
clearly visible [____]
[____] hole
(alight but [____])
[____] mat

simple [____]
set-up
[____]
[____] and [____] flame
[____] hole
(heating)

monitor the [____]

pointing [____]
hold with [____]
at the top
[____] part of the flame

Electric water bath
[____] temperature.
Place vessel so [____] is [____] substance.
Substance warms [____]
[____] temperature —
can't be used to heat [____]

Electric heater
Vessel heats from [____]
[____] plate so [____] to warm evenly.
Set to [____] temperature — can go [____].

You can use scientific drawings to show how [____] is [____] :
gauze
Bunsen burner
[____] mat

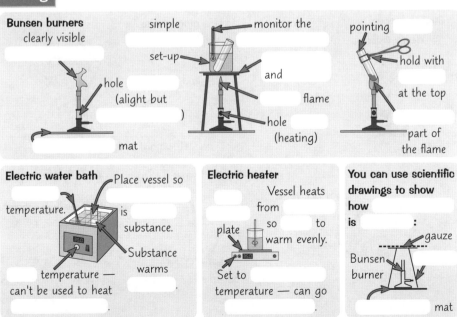

Practical Skills

Safety and Heating Substances

Safety Precautions

Read

Wear

Use a

_____ to
avoid releasing
_____ .

Work in a

Don't handle

Use clamp

Keep away from

Use a

When diluting

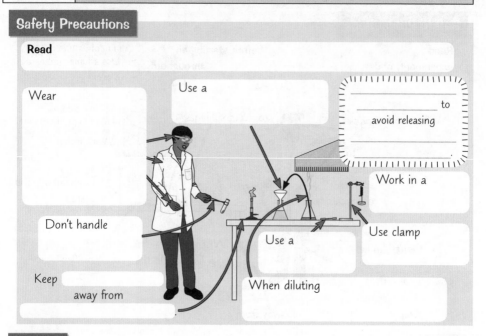

Heating

Bunsen burners
clearly visible

simple _____ monitor the
_____
and _____
_____ flame
_____
(heating)

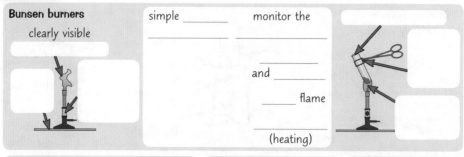

Electric

Place vessel

Set temperature
— _____ .

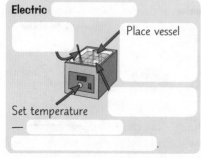

Electric heater
Vessel heats

Set to

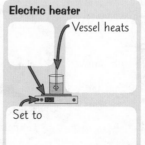

You can use

to show how apparatus
is _____ :

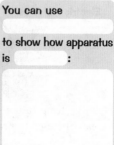

 ☑ ☑ ☑

Water Uptake, Cell Size and Sampling

Five Steps to Measure Rate of Water Uptake

1. Assemble the potometer [____] .

2. Cut the shoot at a [____] underwater and insert it in the [____] .

3. Remove the apparatus from the water, keeping the [____] submerged in the beaker.

4. Remove the [____] from the beaker of water until a single [____] , then put it back in the beaker.

5. As the plant [____] , it takes up water, so the bubble moves along the scale.

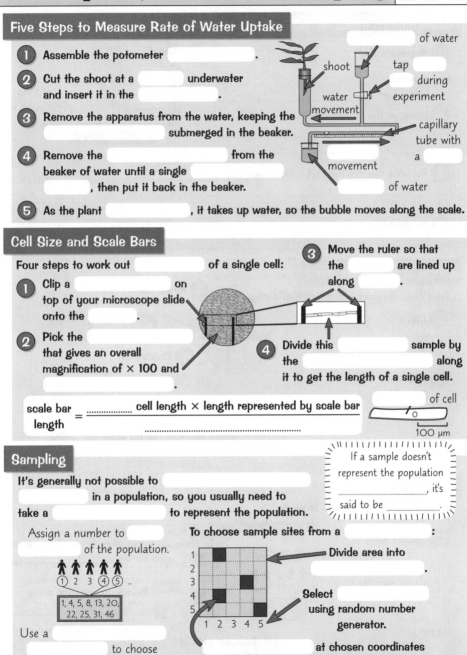

shoot   tap   [____] of water

[____] during experiment

water movement

capillary tube with a [____]

[____] movement

[____] of water

Cell Size and Scale Bars

Four steps to work out [____] of a single cell:

1. Clip a [____] on top of your microscope slide onto the [____] .

2. Pick the [____] that gives an overall magnification of × 100 and [____] .

3. Move the ruler so that the [____] are lined up along [____] .

4. Divide this [____] sample by the [____] along it to get the length of a single cell.

$$\text{scale bar length} = \frac{\text{.............. cell length} \times \text{length represented by scale bar}}{\text{..}}$$

[____] of cell

100 µm

Sampling

It's generally not possible to [____] [____] in a population, so you usually need to take a [____] to represent the population.

If a sample doesn't represent the population [____] , it's said to be [____] .

Assign a number to [____] of the population.

① 2 3 ④ ⑤ ...

1, 4, 5, 8, 13, 20, 22, 25, 31, 46

Use a [____] to choose the sample group.

To choose sample sites from a [____] :

1 2 3 4 5

Divide area into [____] .

Select [____] using random number generator.

[____] at chosen coordinates (e.g. using quadrats or transects).

 ☑ ☑ ☺ ☑

Practical Skills

Water Uptake, Cell Size and Sampling

Five Steps to Measure Rate of Water Uptake

1. Assemble the ....

2. Cut the ....
   and insert ....

3. Remove the apparatus from the water,
   ....
   ....

4. Remove the capillary tube from the ....
   ....
   ....

5. As the plant ....
   ....

movement

during experiment

with a scale

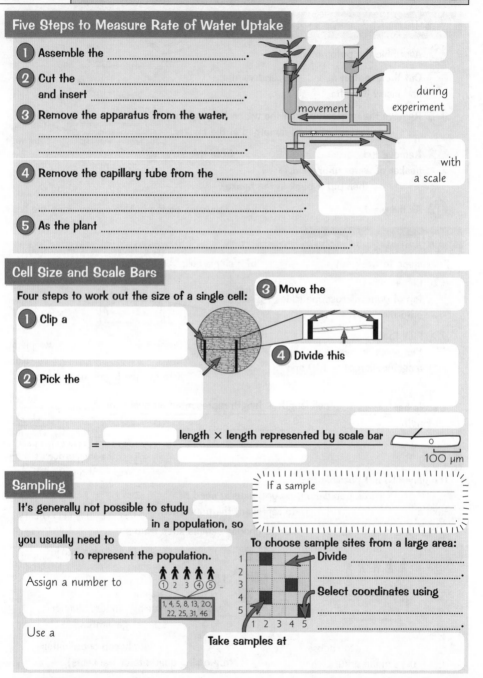

Cell Size and Scale Bars

Four steps to work out the size of a single cell:

1. Clip a

2. Pick the

3. Move the

4. Divide this

$$\boxed{} = \frac{\text{length} \times \text{length represented by scale bar}}{\boxed{}}$$

0

100 μm

Sampling

It's generally not possible to study [ ] [ ] in a population, so you usually need to [ ] [ ] to represent the population.

If a sample ....
....

Assign a number to

👤👤👤👤👤
① 2 3 ④⑤ ...

1, 4, 5, 8, 13, 20, 22, 25, 31, 46

Use a

To choose sample sites from a large area:

Divide ....
....

Select coordinates using ....
....

Take samples at

☹ ✓   🙂 ✓   😊 ✓

Percentage Change, Ethics & Electronics

Percentage Change

To compare results that didn't have the _____, calculate the percentage change:

$$\% \text{ change} = \frac{\text{_____ value} - \text{_____ value}}{\text{original value}} \times 100$$

Ethics

Any organisms used in an _____ need to be treated _____ and _____.

Animals kept _____ should be cared for in a _____ way.

_____ captured for study should be returned to their _____.

Other students shouldn't be _____ _____ into participating in experiments.

Instruments Used in Circuits

Make sure you use an ammeter or voltmeter with an _____, e.g. mA, mV.

Connect a voltmeter in _____ with a device to measure the _____ across it.

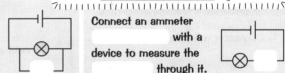

Connect an ammeter _____ with a device to measure the _____ through it.

Multimeters are devices that can measure _____, _____ or _____.

Connect them correctly and turn the dial to _____.

Light Gates

Light beam is shone from _____ to _____.

_____ to computer. Computer measures time that light beam is _____.

Two quantities measured using light gates:

1 Speed Use _____ and time that light beam is broken to _____.

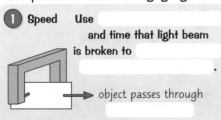

object passes through _____

2 Acceleration Calculate speed of _____ and use this to calculate acceleration. _____ shape of object means _____

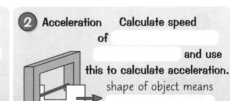

Percentage Change, Ethics & Electronics

Percentage Change

To compare results that ⬚

$$\% \text{ change} = \frac{\boxed{}}{\boxed{} \text{ value}} \times \boxed{}$$

Ethics

Any organisms used ⬚

➤ Animals kept ⬚

➤ Wild animals ⬚

Other students shouldn't be _____ _____ .

Make sure you _____ _____ .

Instruments Used in Circuits

Connect a voltmeter ⬚

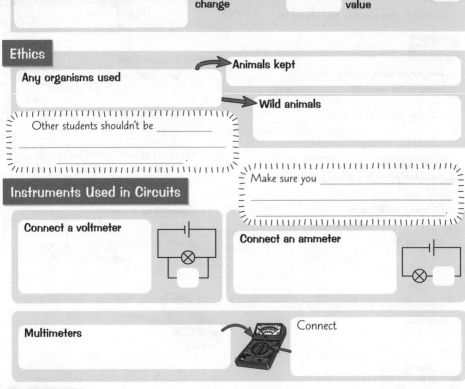

Connect an ammeter ⬚

Multimeters ⬚

Connect ⬚

Light Gates

Light beam ⬚

Detector ⬚

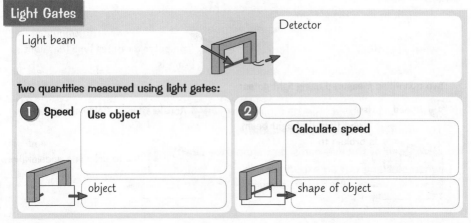

Two quantities measured using light gates:

1 Speed — Use object ⬚

_____ object

2 ⬚

Calculate speed ⬚

_____ shape of object

Practical Skills

 ☑ ☑ ☑

Mixed Practice Quizzes

The final quiz pages of the book... Hooray! Before you start celebrating, use them to check you know all of the practical skills covered on p.305-314.

Quiz 1   Date: ...... / ...... / ......

1) Give two examples of when you'd use indicator paper.

2) What is a biased sample?

3) Give one way you can ensure you are working safely with hot glassware.

4) Describe how to use a measuring cylinder to collect gaseous products.

5) Name the apparatus used for measuring the angle between two lines.

6) What is a potometer used to measure?

7) How can you ensure that a sample is heated evenly by an electric heater?

8) Give an example of when a scientific drawing may be used.

9) True or false? An ammeter should be always be connected in parallel with the device it is measuring.

10) Why might using a gas syringe to measure the volume of gas be more accurate than an upturned measuring cylinder?

Total:

Quiz 2   Date: ...... / ...... / ......

1) Describe how to read the volume of a liquid from a scale.

2) What piece of apparatus could you use to measure temperature?

3) Give an advantage of using a pH probe and meter over universal indicator.

4) What is the hottest part of a Bunsen burner flame?

5) Give two ways of heating a sample without using a flame.

6) What is a eureka can used for?

7) Give a safety precaution you should follow when using flammable chemicals.

8) What is the neutral pH value?

9) True or false? Wild animals captured for study should not be returned to their original habitat.

10) Give three protective items that should be worn when carrying out an experiment.

Total:

Mixed Practice Quizzes

Date: ...... / ...... / ......

1) Describe how to use a light gate to measure the acceleration of an object.
2) Describe how a Bunsen burner should look when it is alight but not heating.
3) Give two ways of accurately transferring a mass of solid to a reaction vessel.
4) Describe how a shoot should be cut before it is inserted in a potometer.
5) What device is capable of measuring either current or potential difference?
6) How can you avoid releasing harmful gases in a reaction into the room?
7) Describe how to take a random sample from a population of people.
8) What piece of apparatus can transfer a specific volume of liquid?
9) What can be used help to seal a system when collecting the gaseous products of a reaction in a filled, upturned measuring cylinder?
10) Compare the heating capabilities of water baths and electric heaters.

Total:

Quiz 4   Date: ...... / ...... / ......

1) Give the equation for percentage change.
2) When heating a substance in a boiling tube, how should the tube be angled to ensure it is being heated safely?
3) When using a ruler, what can you use to make sure you always measure length from the same point?
4) True or false? When diluting a liquid, the water should be added to the concentrated substance.
5) How should you place a vessel in a water bath so that its contents are heated evenly?
6) What must be considered when picking a suitably sized measuring cylinder?
7) How should the hole on a Bunsen burner be set when it is used for heating?
8) Describe how to measure the length of a cell using a microscope.
9) How does bubbling gas into a measuring cylinder that has been filled and upturned in a beaker of water allow you to measure its volume?
10) Give one example of when and why you might use a funnel in an experiment.

Total:

SCAFNR41